Exercise and Test Book

The Writer's Workplace

SEVENTH EDITION

and

The Writer's Workplace with Readings

FIFTH EDITION

Sandra Scarry
Formerly with the Office of Academic Affairs,
City University of New York

John Scarry
Hostos Community College,
City University of New York

Prepared by
Valerie Russell
Valencia Community College

THOMSON

WADSWORTH

Australia • Canada • Mexico • Singapore • Spain
United Kingdom • United States

Ju ⊃ ₂ ₀ᵤ₀

Exercise and Test Book
The Writer's Workplace, Seventh Edition
The Writer's Workplace with Readings, Fifth Edition
Sandra Scarry / John Scarry
Prepared by Valerie Russell

Publisher: *Michael Rosenberg*
Acquisitions Editor: *Stephen Dalphin*
Development Editor: *Laurie Runion*
Production Project Manager: *Samantha Ross*
Executive Marketing Manager: *Carrie Brandon*

Manufacturing Manager: *Marcia Locke*
Compositor/Project Manager: *G & S Book Services*
Cover Designer: *Brian Salisbury*
Printer: *Darby Printing Company*
Cover Illustration: © *Jay Montgomery 2003*

Printed in the United States of America.

2   3   4   5   07   06   05

For more information contact Thomson Wadsworth,
25 Thomson Place, Boston, MA 02210 USA, or you can
visit our Internet site at *http://www.thomson.com*

For permission to use material from this
text or product, submit a request online at
http://www.thomsonrights.com

Any additional questions about permissions can be
submitted by email to thomsonrights@thomson.com

ISBN: 1-4130-0250-1

Acknowledgments

I want to thank the authors, John and Sandra Scarry, for this opportunity. For years, I have
used and loved their book, and to get the chance to be a part of it is wonderful. Thanks also
to my students throughout the years who have helped me become a better, more thorough
teacher, which made me ready for this challenge. And to S. and B., thanks for allowing me the
time to get this project done and the encouragement to know that I could do it; you are my
inspiration.

Valerie Russell
Valencia Community College

Contents

Part II: Parallel Structure and Modifiers   94

Practicing More with Verbs   107

Using Correct Capitalization and Punctuation   121

Paying Attention to Look-Alikes and Sound-Alikes   140

Answers   151

Correcting Fragments and Run-ons   165

Making Sentence Parts Work Together   168

Part I: Pronouns   168

Part II: Parallel Structure and Modifiers   170

Practicing More with Verbs   173

Using Correct Capitalization and Punctuation   **175**

Paying Attention to Look-Alikes and Sound-Alikes   **179**

Tests and Exercises

Finding Subjects and Verbs in Simple Sentences

Diagnostic Test

Find the subject and the verb in each sentence. Choose the letter (A, B, or C) that contains both the correct subject and verb.

1. None of the lunches is ready to eat yet.
   A. lunches, is
   B. none, is
   C. none, ready

2. There are more suggestions in his report.
   A. suggestions, are
   B. there, are
   C. more, are

3. At the meeting, we will discuss my job description.
   A. meeting, job
   B. we, will
   C. we, will discuss

4. After all the discussion, Marcy had to admit her feelings.
   A. Marcy, had
   B. discussion, had
   C. Marcy, admit

5. Does that girl have any more hotdogs to sell?
   A. hotdogs, sell
   B. girl, have
   C. girl, does have

6. Why can I not write a good question?
   A. why, can
   B. I, can not
   C. I, can write

7. The boys, along with their fathers, got into the fishing boat.
   A. boys, got
   B. boys/fathers, got
   C. fathers, got

8. Please leave your homework on the desk.
   A. homework, leave
   B. please, leave
   C. (you), leave

9. The president of the college, a former banker, delivered the graduation address.
   A. president, delivered
   B. banker, delivered
   C. graduation, delivered

10. The brilliant chemist devised a new, moneymaking formula.
    A. brilliant chemist, devised
    B. formula, moneymaking
    C. chemist, devised

Exercise A

Determine the subject in each of the following sentences by asking yourself the "who or what" question. Don't forget to identify the verb first.

1. With sprinting speeds of about 65 mph, the cheetah is the fastest animal on land.
   (Who or what is the fastest animal?)
   The subject is _____

2. The cheetah's incredible speed depends on some finely adaptive features.
   (Who or what depends on adaptive features?)
   The subject is _____

3. The cheetah's legs, longer than those of other cats, are its most obvious feature.
   (Who or what is its most obvious feature?)
   The subject is _____

4. Their long shoulder blades work with their legs to achieve single strides of 20 feet or more.
   (Who or what work?)
   The subject is _____

5. Enlarged nostrils and a wide airway deliver lots of air to this fast runner.
   (Who or what deliver lots of air?)
   The subject is _____

6. The cheetah's powerful lungs allow the running animal to breathe deeply.
   (Who or what allow the running animal to breathe?)
   The subject is _____

7. Unlike those of other cats, the cheetah's claws are always strong and blunt.
   (Who or what are strong and blunt?)
   The subject is _____

8. The cheetah's claws help the animal to push off and build speed fast.
   (Who or what help to push off?)
   The subject is _____

9. This feature most resembles Olympic runners' track shoes.
   (Who or what most resembles?)
   The subject is _____

10. The pad at the foot's center catches the ground, much the same as a tire tread.
    (Who or what catches the ground?)
    The subject is _____

Exercise B

Read each sentence and decide which answer (A, B, or C) correctly indicates the subject and verb.

1. The cheetah's hard toe pads help the runner to stop suddenly.
    A. runner, stop
    B. toe pads, help
    C. toe pads, stop

2. Cheetahs can turn or stop suddenly by widely spreading their toes.
    A. cheetahs, can spread
    B. cheetahs, spreading
    C. cheetahs, can turn (or) stop

3. A cheetah can suddenly stop a stride as fast as 20 mph.
    A. stride, can stop
    B. cheetah, stop
    C. cheetah, can stop

4. Extraordinary speed, sudden turning, and quick stopping make the cheetah a great hunter.
    A. speed, make
    B. cheetah, make
    C. speed, turning (and) stopping, make

5. A herd of gazelles can be most vulnerable to a speeding cheetah.
    A. herd, can be
    B. gazelles, can be
    C. cheetah, can be

6. The chosen gazelle is struck by the cheetah's forepaw.
    A. gazelle, is struck
    B. cheetah, is
    C. forepaw, is

7. The prey falls from its feet before the hunter.
    A. hunter, falls
    B. feet, falls
    C. prey, falls

8. Then, finally, the cheetah clamps its powerful jaws shut over the gazelle's throat.
    A. jaws, shut
    B. cheetah, clamps
    C. throat, clamps

9. In spite of the cheetah's speed, larger and stronger animals can be a challenge.
    A. animals, can be
    B. speed, can
    C. animals, challenge

10. Lions can often steal a cheetah's kill, adding to the cheetah's efforts at satisfying its own hunger.
    A. lions, can steal
    B. efforts, satisfying
    C. cheetah's kill

11. Lions can also be a considerable threat to cheetah cubs.
    A. lions, threat
    B. lions, can be
    C. cheetah cubs, can be

12. Vulnerable to the larger lions, a diminishing number of cubs survive to grow to maturity.
    A. cubs, survive
    B. number, survive
    C. cubs, grow

13. Conservationists have recently taken note of the cheetahs' decrease in numbers.
    A. conservationists, note
    B. numbers, decrease
    C. conservationists, have taken note

14. However, these biologists are optimistic about the growing cheetah population.
    A. biologists, are growing
    B. biologists, are
    C. population, are growing

15. Habitation in areas with fewer large animals is the cheetah's best chance.
    A. Habitation, is
    B. chance, is
    C. areas, is

Exercise C

In the following passage, underline the subject of each sentence once and underline the verb twice.

Miami, a city with miles of beaches amid many high-priced neighborhoods, is my hometown. With an average of 359 days of sunshine every year, it has become a leading winter resort. Not surprisingly, tourism continues to be the largest source of income. In the 1960s and in 1980, large numbers of Cubans immigrated to Miami. The city now has the largest Cuban community in the United States. The flavor of the Latin American culture adds to the charm of the city. In addition to tourism, the metropolis holds a place of importance as a business and financial center. This port of entry is a terminal for the vast air and sea trade with Latin America. Many business and financial firms have their headquarters in Miami. My fondest memories of Miami will always be of the days sunning, picnicing, and playing Frisbee on the beach.

Exercise D

In the following passage, underline the subject of each sentence once and underline the verb twice.

The most common type of giraffe is the reticulated giraffe. Its colors have a clear pattern of white lines surrounding the darker brown spots. With their speed, adult animals are relatively safe from predators. Additionally, the giraffe's large hooves also help in its defense. A kick from an adult giraffe can be deadly for predators as fierce as lions. However, in order to drink, the giraffe must lower its head down to the water. To do this, the giraffe spreads its long legs to lower itself. In this position, the giraffe is vulnerable to attack.

Exercise E

In the following passage, underline the subject of each sentence once and underline the verb twice.

At the spring recital, the young pianist performed Beethoven's "Moonlight Sonata." The audience remained motionless. In the dark concert hall, there was not even the rustling of a program. The soloist sat alone in the spotlight on the stage. The young man was a first year student from New York. His entrance to the music academy had depended on a scholarship. His interpretation of Beethoven's music then had impressed his masters. Now they also remarked on the emotional intensity of his performance. At the end of the sonata, he stood, turned, and bowed to the audience. The thunderous applause lit up his boyish face.

Exercise F

In the following paragraphs, underline the subject of each sentence once and underline the verb twice.

I love movies, especially comedies. Movies can take me to other countries or other times. *Robin Hood: Men in Tights*, one of Mel Brooks' films, is one of my favorites and features Cary Elwes and Richard Lewis. At Christmas, I enjoy watching *Scrooged* with Bill Murray. Bill Murray plays the Ebenezer Scrooge part. He is a television executive. Romantic comedies, like *When Harry Met Sally*, and *Roxanne*, represent another category of my favorites. *When Harry Met Sally*, featuring Billy Crystal and Meg Ryan, chronicles a couple's romantic journey to the altar. Steve Martin with a huge fake nose is the star of *Roxanne*, a modern day Cyrano de Bergerac. Everyone needs a good laugh. Laughing makes me feel less stressed.

Mastery Test

Find the subject and the verb in each sentence. Choose the answer (A, B, or C) that contains both the correct subject and verb.

1. Species conservation is a crucial component in recent efforts at maintaining zoo animal population.
    A. efforts, maintaining
    B. conservation, is
    C. species conservation, is crucial

2. Programs of exchanging animals among different zoos for mating have become popular.
    A. animals, have become
    B. programs, have become
    C. zoos, have become

3. These programs help to alleviate the problems of inbreeding.
    A. programs, help
    B. problems, alleviate
    C. inbreeding, alleviate

4. Related animals, often residents of the same zoo, carry similar genes.
    A. residents, carry
    B. genes, carry
    C. animals, carry

5. In the mating of related animals, similar genes combine.
    A. genes, combine
    B. mating, genes
    C. animals, combine

6. Inbred offspring are more vulnerable to deformation and disease.
    A. deformation and disease, are
    B. offspring, are
    C. offspring, are more vulnerable

7. Animals from different zoos can be paired with the exchange program.
    A. zoos, can be
    B. different zoos, can be
    C. animals, can be paired

8. Genetic diversity, which is naturally present in the wild, can be achieved by the program.
    A. program, can be achieved
    B. wild, can be achieved
    C. diversity, can be achieved

9. Healthier animal offspring are born.
    A. animal, are born
    B. animal offspring, are born
    C. offspring, are born

10. Through these efforts, genetic diversity in the zoo habitat can be preserved.
    A. diversity, can be preserved
    B. efforts, can be preserved
    C. habitat, can be preserved

Making Subjects and Verbs Agree

Diagnostic Test

Each sentence contains a blank to indicate a missing verb. Choose the answer (A or B) that shows the correct form of the verb.

1. They _____ at everything.
    A. laughs
    B. laugh

2. Everyone in the group _____ to attend.
    A. expects
    B. expect

3. There _____ few who will agree.
    A. is
    B. are

4. The committee seldom _____ about anything. (Consider the group as individuals.)
    A. agrees
    B. agree

5. He _____ like movies.
    A. doesn't
    B. don't

6. Either my friend or my relatives _____ treating me to dinner.
    A. is
    B. are

7. Many of the townspeople _____ about the dress code.
    A. cares
    B. care

8. _____ the jury reached a verdict? (Consider the group as a unit.)
    A. Has
    B. Have

9. Nobody _____ special consideration.
    A. gets
    B. get

10. Where _____ the treasures hidden?
    A. was
    B. were

Exercise A

Each sentence contains a blank. Choose the form of the verb (A or B) that correctly completes the sentence.

1. Vital to the body as the brain and lungs, the heart _____ to pump the blood around the body.
    A. beats
    B. beat

2. This circulation of blood, performed by one of the body's involuntary muscles, _____ essential to healthy function.
    A. is
    B. are

3. Pericardial fluid _____ the space around the heart called the pericardium.
    A. fills
    B. fill

4. The heart, like all muscles, _____ constant blood supply.
    A. requires
    B. require

5. The coronary arteries _____ blood supplied with oxygen and nutrients to the heart.
    A. takes
    B. take

6. Capillaries within the heart _____ blood to every part of the large muscle.
    A. carries
    B. carry

7. The blood carrying away the waste products _____ the heart through the coronary veins.
    A. leaves
    B. leave

8. The cells within every part of the human body _____ oxygen and nutrients to survive.
    A. needs
    B. need

9. Healthy cells _____ immunity against disease-causing germs.
    A. requires
    B. require

10. The heart, together with blood vessels and the blood, _____ to sustain healthy cell function.
    A. works
    B. work

Exercise B

Each sentence contains a blank. Choose the form of the verb (A or B) that correctly completes the sentence.

1. About the size of a fist, the heart _____ as a pump supplying all the body's systems with blood.
    A. acts
    B. act

2. The heart _____ actually two separate pumps.
    A. is
    B. are

3. The right and left sides of the heart _____ blood to the lungs and the rest of the body.
    A. supplies
    B. supply

4. The septum _____ the two sides of the heart.
    A. separates
    B. separate

5. Separation of the two sides _____ necessary to prevent passage of the blood from side to side.
    A. is
    B. are

6. Each of the two sides _____ two chambers.
    A. has
    B. have

7. The upper chambers, called the atria, _____ above the lower chambers, called the ventricles.
    A. lies
    B. lie

8. From atrium to ventricle, blood flow through the heart _____ a one-way process.
    A. is
    B. are

9. Valves, which are flaps of tissue, _____ the direction of the flow.
    A. controls
    B. control

10. Flaps of the valve _____ flattened against the vein wall toward the direction of the flow.
    A. is
    B. are

11. In the case of backward flow of blood, the flaps _____ back in place to cause a block.
    A. shuts
    B. shut

12. The action of these flaps _____ much like the opening and closing of doors.
    A. is
    B. are

13. Channels for blood flow _____ opened when the valves relax.
    A. is
    B. are

14. However, with the contraction of valves, the flow of blood _____ blocked.
    A. is
    B. are

15. The flaps of the valve _____ held in place by strong tendons.
    A. is
    B. are

Exercise C

Each sentence contains a blank. Choose the form of the verb (A or B) that correctly completes the sentence.

1. Veronica, along with her teammates, _____ not appear happy.
    A. does
    B. do

2. The softball team _____ a stiff competitor.
    (Consider the group as a unit.)
    A. faces
    B. face

3. The girls on the team _____ tried to win each game.
    A. has
    B. have

4. However, they _____ not always win.
    A. does
    B. do

5. Now, the team on the field with them _____ ahead.
    A. is
    B. are

6. There _____ many fans watching the game.
    A. is
    B. are

7. _____ the teams know the reputation of the coach?
    A. Does
    B. Do

8. Here _____ a fast ball!
    A. comes
    B. come

9. The pitcher _____ to first base to try to catch the runner.
    A. throws
    B. throw

10. Fortunately, the first base player _____ paying attention.
    A. is
    B. are

11. The players _____ chatter to the batter.
    A. barks
    B. bark

12. Veronica's teammates _____ as the batter strikes out.
    A. cheers
    B. cheer

13. Hot dogs and chips _____ the main meal for the fans.
    A. is
    B. are

14. At all the practices, Veronica's coach _____ the team.
    A. encourages
    B. encourage

15. Neither the team nor the coach _____ planning a late night celebration.
    A. is
    B. are

Exercise D

Choose the sentence (A or B) that contains subject-verb agreement.

1. A. Neither Sergio nor Juan have been chosen for the award.
    B. Neither Sergio nor Juan has been chosen for the award.

2. A. Sergio, the taller of the two men, have dark brown hair.
    B. Sergio, the taller of the two men, has dark brown hair.

3. A. Juan, the youngest of my brothers, has dyed his hair yellow blonde.
    B. Juan, the youngest of my brothers, have dyed his hair yellow blonde.

4. A. Salsa and chips is their favorite snack.
    B. Salsa and chips are their favorite snack.

5. A. Sergio and Juan loves to salsa.
    B. Sergio and Juan love to salsa.

6. A. One of Sergio's favorite partners are Gloria.
    B. One of Sergio's favorite partners is Gloria.

7. A. Gloria and Clarita usually wears red, flowing dresses.
    B. Gloria and Clarita usually wear red, flowing dresses.

8. A. Denise or Betty is Juan's favorite partner.
    B. Denise or Betty are Juan's favorite partner.

9. A. Was you going to the dance?
    B. Were you going to the dance?

10. A. Someone in the group are the leader.
    B. Someone in the group is the leader.

11. A. Everyone in the group, including Hernando, enjoys dancing salsa.
    B. Everyone in the group, including Hernando, enjoy dancing salsa.

12. A. All of the missing costumes was found.
    B. All of the missing costumes were found.

13. A. She don't seem to care about the outcome of the contest.
    B. She doesn't seem to care about the outcome of the contest.

14. A. What time does the movie begin tonight?
    B. What time do the movie begin tonight?

15. A. The girls and Hernando plans to meet at seven o'clock.
    B. The girls and Hernando plan to meet at seven o'clock.

Exercise E

In the paragraph below, choose the correct verb form for each of the sentences.

Montreal, the City of Festivals, (is, are) alive with street parties and celebrations. The

people of Montreal (ranks, rank) high among the world's supporters of urban festivals.

Festivals such as the Annual Jazz Fest and the World Film Festival (accounts, account)

for just a few. A crowd (gathers, gather) at the appearance of a street band. A pair

of comfortable shoes (is, are) essential for anyone touring historic Old Montreal.

Everybody (finds, find) something to enjoy in Montreal's dining establishments. These

restaurants, cafes, and bistros (offers, offer) the cuisine of several nationalities. At the

Biodome de Montreal, visitors (explores, explore) re-creations of natural ecosystems.

The Botanical Garden, with over thirty gardens, (is, are) a popular touring site.

Montreal's chic boulevards and 18-mile Underground City (delights, delight) shoppers.

Exercise F

In the paragraph below, choose the correct verb form for each of the sentences.

Each of the committee members (works, work) the whole afternoon to get ready for the dance. Everyone in the group (has, have) a different task. There (is, are) so much to be done before the class arrives. The committee chairperson (doesn't, don't) feel confident. However, the members on the committee (keeps, keep) up the pace to turn the gym into a dance hall. The sound and the lights (is, are) checked. Streamers and banners (adds, add) color and design to the pale blue walls of the gym. (Does, Do) the banners announce the special occasion? "The Spring Fling" banner, painted in pastels, (stretches, stretch) across the far wall. Who (is, are) the artists of such beautiful artwork?

Mastery Test

Each sentence contains a blank. Choose the form of the verb (A or B) that correctly completes the sentence.

1. Sue's children and husband _____ her to go with him on a cruise.
    A. wants
    B. want

2. The laptops in our computer lab _____ 17-inch monitors.
    A. has
    B. have

3. The concert pianist unlike some of the other instrumental musicians _____ every day.
    A. practices
    B. practice

4. The boys in the band _____ several instruments.
    A. plays
    B. play

5. During the movie, either Jason or Brian _____ the popcorn.
    A. buys
    B. buy

6. Turning the corner, both the driver of the bus and I _____ too late to avoid the truck.
    A. was
    B. were

7. In the spring, the crocus or the daffodil _____ the first to bloom.
    A. is
    B. are

8. The guest list for the upcoming parties _____ some very famous people.
    A. includes
    B. include

9. There _____ some great new songs on that CD.
    A. is
    B. are

10. The girl, along with her mother, _____ at the fancy mall.
    A. shops
    B. shop

Understanding Fragments and Phrases

Diagnostic Test

Identify the underlined phrases in each of the following sentences. Choose from the following (answers may be used more than once):

A. noun phrase
B. prepositional phrase
C. verb phrase
D. infinitive phrase
E. participial phrase
F. gerund phrase

_____ 1. Monet was one <u>of the most important figures</u> of French impressionism.

_____ 2. He <u>successfully captured</u> the colors of nature.

_____ 3. <u>To recreate and intensify the natural luminosity of light</u>, Monet stroked small dabs of pure contrasting colors onto his canvases.

_____ 4. <u>Using this technique</u>, Monet achieved a new vibrancy and glow.

_____ 5. Monet is especially famous for his studies of one subject <u>at different times of day</u>.

_____ 6. <u>The St. Lazare train station</u> is one of these famous studies.

_____ 7. <u>Painting outdoors</u> was encouraged by his childhood teacher.

_____ 8. <u>His early style</u> was realistic.

_____ 9. However, he soon identified himself <u>with the Impressionists</u>.

_____ 10. His revolutionary ideas <u>were frequently rejected</u> by the public.

Exercise A

Identify the underlined phrases in each of the following sentences. Choose from the following (answers may be used more than once):

    A. noun phrase
    B. prepositional phrase
    C. verb phrase
    D. infinitive phrase
    E. participial phrase
    F. gerund phrase

_____   1.   Walter Frederick Mondale first became <u>a national figure</u> in the late 1960s and early 1970s.

_____   2.   <u>Representing the people of Minnesota</u>, he was a leading liberal on domestic issues.

_____   3.   In 1976, presidential hopeful Jimmy Carter needed a northern liberal <u>to balance his ticket</u>.

_____   4.   He <u>wisely chose</u> Senator Walter "Fritz" Mondale as his running mate.

_____   5.   <u>After the election</u>, Mondale was an influential Vice President.

_____   6.   Carter <u>often called</u> him his "partner."

_____   7.   In 1984, <u>overcoming a strong challenge from Gary Hart</u>, Mondale won the Democratic nomination.

_____   8.   He had the support <u>from organized labor and party regulars</u>.

_____   9.   <u>Choosing Geraldine Ferraro as his running mate</u> was a historic moment.

_____ 10.   She was the first woman named <u>to a major party ticket</u>.

_____ 11.   He was running <u>against an enormously popular incumbent president, Ronald Reagan</u>.

_____ 12.   Mondale was a cautious politician <u>with a stiff and formal style</u>.

_____ 13.   President Reagan had <u>superb television skills</u>.

_____ 14.   Mondale's candidacy <u>never caught</u> fire.

_____ 15.   <u>Receiving only 41 percent of the popular vote</u>, he was overwhelmingly defeated by Ronald Reagan.

Exercise B

Each of the following groups of words is a fragment. Identify what is missing and needs to be added in order to make the fragment into a sentence.

    A.   Add a subject
    B.   Add a verb
    C.   Add a subject and a verb
    D.   The subject and verb are present, but it doesn't express a complete thought.

_____ 1.   many Americans' favorite game of baseball

_____ 2.   after the excitement of football season

_____ 3.   is a game played with a bat, a ball, and a glove

_____ 4.   baseball is, above all other sports,

_____ 5.   the game is played by

_____ 6.   two teams, each with nine players,

_____ 7.   bat and play the field

_____ 8.   the field's main divisions are

_____ 9.   the infield

_____ 10. with dirt

Exercise C

Each of the following groups of words is a fragment. Identify what is missing and needs to be added in order to make the fragment into a sentence.

    A.   Add a subject
    B.   Add a verb
    C.   Add a subject and a verb
    D.   The subject and verb are present, but it doesn't express a complete thought.

_____ 1.   the geometric perfection of the infield

_____ 2.   can be admired from a fortunate fan's seat location

_____ 3.   is a perfect square area measuring 90 feet by 90 feet

_____ 4.   at each corner of the area is

_____ 5.   exactly 90 feet from each other

_____ 6.   measures 15 inches square

_____ 7.   a rubber five-sided mat

_____ 8.   serve to mark boundaries on either side of home plate

_____ 9.   stands inside the batter's box on either the left or right side

_____ 10. the catcher's box is marked off with

_____ 11. in the batter's box

_____ 12. awaits the pitch

_____ 13. steps up to the plate

_____ 14. only two inches at the widest part

_____ 15. one of the toughest challenges in sports

Exercise D

Each of the following groups of words is a fragment. Identify what is missing and needs to be added in order to make the fragment into a sentence.

    A.   Add a subject
    B.   Add a verb
    C.   Add a subject and a verb
    D.   The subject and verb are present, but it doesn't express a complete thought.

_____ 1.   became known as the great "Babe" or Babe Ruth

_____ 2.   in the beginning he

_____ 3.   his average

_____ 4.   a rare accomplishment

_____ 5.   his famous skill

_____ 6.   turned him into a baseball legend

_____ 7.   had his quite humble beginning in Baltimore

_____ 8.   on February 6, 1895

_____ 9.   he lived in

_____ 10.   young Ruth soon became

_____ 11.   his cursing, tobacco chewing, and running wild

_____ 12.   placed him in St. Mary's Industrial School in Baltimore

_____ 13.   homeless, runaway, unwanted, or delinquent boys

_____ 14.   at St. Mary's, Ruth received

_____ 15.   with Jack Dunn of the Orioles in 1914

Exercise E

Each of the following groups of words is a fragment. Identify what is missing and needs to be added in order to make the fragment into a sentence.

    A.   Add a subject
    B.   Add a verb
    C.   Add a subject and a verb
    D.   The subject and verb are present, but it doesn't express a complete thought.

_____   1.   Aaron's birth date was

_____   2.   like Babe Ruth, Aaron was born

_____   3.   in 1934 hospitals did not admit

_____   4.   was a poor family, much like the Ruth family

_____   5.   Aaron's love of baseball

_____   6.   like Babe Ruth, from early on, Aaron

_____   7.   black players formed

_____   8.   tried out for the Mobile Bears and played shortstop

_____   9.   with the Mobile Bears

_____ 10.   at 16, Aaron

_____ 11.   signed Jackie Robinson in 1947

_____ 12.   was the first black player to join the majors

_____ 13.   boarded a train for Winston-Salem to play with the Indianapolis Clowns

_____ 14.   traveled the country playing the best local black teams

_____ 15.   Aaron proved

Exercise F

Rewrite the following groups of words, changing each fragment into a sentence.

1. the mountain climber on top of the mountain

   _____

   _____

2. stopping me, the traveler

   _____

   _____

3. in a red scarf around her neck

   _____

   _____

4. should be kept in the refrigerator

   _____

   _____

5. the book is

   _____

   _____

6. I wanted to

   _____

   _____

7. the baseball in the display case

   _____

   _____

8. I did not see

   _____

   _____

9.   dressed all in green

_____

_____

10. the old-fashioned ice cream social

_____

_____

Exercise G

Rewrite the following paragraph, correcting all fragment errors.

Understanding the very basic science of leaf coloration. This can make observation more interesting. The gradual, but quite dazzling, color changes among the leaves of deciduous trees like oaks, hickories, sumacs, maples, aspens, and gums. Occurring only in America's temperate zones. Among these areas, the display in the East especially brilliant in its colors of autumn foliage. Exceptionally breathtaking views can be seen by travelers on New England roadway tours. The sugar maples ablaze in fiery red. This incredible backdrop of color. Impressing vacationers for countless autumn seasons.

_____

_____

_____

_____

_____

_____

_____

_____

_____

Mastery Test

Rewrite the following groups of words, changing each fragment into a complete sentence.

1. to be in line today

    _____

    _____

2. the young man with time off from work

    _____

    _____

3. he wants to purchase

    _____

    _____

4. he loves

    _____

    _____

5. have a new center and a new point guard

    _____

    _____

6. the coach begins practice on

    _____

    _____

7. the season ticket holders get to sit in

    _____

    _____

8. watch from the seats in the upper deck

    _____

    _____

9. for the best tickets

    _____

    _____

10. pizza and soft drinks

    _____

    _____

Combining Sentences Using Three Options for Coordination

Diagnostic Test

Each of the following sentence pairs could be combined using coordination. For each pair, choose the answer (A, B, or C) that shows which sentence has been combined correctly.

1. There are two types of sequoia in California. They are both impressively grand.
    A. There are two types of sequoia in California and they are both impressively grand.
    B. There are two types of sequoia in California, they are both impressively grand.
    C. There are two types of sequoia in California, and they are both impressively grand.

2. One species is called *sequoia sempervirens.* The other is called *sequoia gigantea.*
    A. One species is called *sequoia sempervirens;* the other is called *sequoia gigantea.*
    B. One species is called *sequoia sempervirens,* the other is called *sequoia gigantea.*
    C. One species is called *sequoia sempervirens* and the other is called *sequoia gigantea.*

3. *Sequoia sempervirens,* or coast redwood, grows in thick groves. Very little sunlight reaches the ground beneath.
    A. *Sequoia sempervirens,* or coast redwood, grows in thick groves, so very little sunlight reaches the ground beneath.
    B. *Sequoia sempervirens,* or coast redwood, grows in thick groves, therefore very little sunlight reaches the ground beneath.
    C. *Sequoia sempervirens,* or coast redwood, grows in thick groves so very little sunlight reaches the ground beneath.

4. The groves are thick and dark. The trees are among the highest in the world.
    A. Either the groves are thick and dark or the trees are among the highest in the world.
    B. Not only are the groves thick and dark, but also the trees are among the highest in the world.
    C. The groves are thick and dark, the trees are among the highest in the world.

5. I brought along good hiking gear. I went primarily to walk in the woods among these giant trees.
    A. I brought along good hiking gear, however I went primarily to walk in the woods among these giant trees.
    B. I brought along good hiking gear, for I went primarily to walk in the woods among these giant trees.
    C. I brought along good hiking gear and I went primarily to walk in the woods among these giant trees.

6. The bark of these enormous giants can be two feet thick. Tracing your finger along its grooves is fascinating.
    A. The bark of these enormous giants can be two feet thick, but tracing your finger along its grooves is fascinating.
    B. The bark of these enormous giants can be two feet thick, or tracing your finger along its grooves is fascinating.
    C. The bark of these enormous giants can be two feet thick; in fact, tracing your finger along its grooves is fascinating.

7. The other species is found in the Sierra. It is the *sequoia gigantea,* or sierra redwood.
    A. The other species is found in the Sierra, it is the *sequoia gigantea,* or sierra redwood.
    B. The other species is found in the Sierra; it is the *sequoia gigantea,* or sierra redwood.
    C. The other species is found in the Sierra it is the *sequoia gigantea,* or sierra redwood.

8. These grow more apart from each other. The bright sunshine can brighten the forest floor.
    A. These grow more apart from each other, but the bright sunshine can brighten the forest floor.
    B. These grow more apart from each other, so the bright sunshine can brighten the forest floor.
    C. These grow more apart from each other, the bright sunshine can brighten the forest floor.

9. They are pointed at the top like cones. They have been broken at the top by storms.
    A. They are pointed at the top like cones, they have been broken at the top by storms.
    B. They are pointed at the top like cones or they have been broken at the top by storms.
    C. Either they are pointed at the top like cones, or they have been broken at the top by storms.

10. Walking in any forest can be delightful. Walking beneath the coast redwoods is awe inspiring.
    A. Walking in any forest can be delightful; however, walking beneath the coast redwoods is awe inspiring.
    B. Walking in any forest can be delightful but walking beneath the coast redwoods is awe inspiring.
    C. Walking in any forest can be delightful but, walking beneath the coast redwoods is awe inspiring.

Exercise A

Each of the following examples contains two simple sentences that could be combined with a coordinating conjunction. In each case, choose which coordinating conjunction best combines the two sentences (A, B, or C).

1.   Vehicles come in all shapes and sizes. Buying a new vehicle involves many decisions.
      A.   or
      B.   yet
      C.   so

2.   The first decision concerns what kind of vehicle to buy. You can choose a car, a truck, an SUV, or a van.
      A.   nor (can you choose)
      B.   for
      C.   but

3.   With cars, you can choose a compact model. You can choose a full-size model.
      A.   nor (can you choose)
      B.   or
      C.   so

4.   Then, you might decide on the engine size. You might also decide on the desire for good gas mileage.
      A.   so
      B.   and
      C.   yet

5.   You do not need to base your car buying decision on something like color. You do not want to base your choice on what your friends think.
      A.   nor (do you want)
      B.   so
      C.   but

6.   The options your vehicle can have may be a factor. You should make a list of these options.
      A.   but
      B.   for
      C.   so

7.   Price is a major factor for most people. Some people ask for only the monthly payment amount.
      A.   yet
      B.   nor
      C.   and

8.   The first place to look for information on prices and options is the manufacturer's website. You can "build" a car on some websites.
      A.   for
      B.   but
      C.   or

9. Many dealerships have their own websites. These sites may not give you accurate information on a vehicle's availability at the dealership.
    A. but
    B. or
    C. nor

10. Walking into a dealership can be overwhelming. You should be prepared with a list of questions.
    A. so
    B. for
    C. or

11. At some dealerships, salespeople approach you immediately. At other dealerships, you can walk around without being bothered.
    A. so
    B. but
    C. for

12. Women customers prefer to buy a car from a woman salesperson. Dealerships should hire more women salespersons.
    A. yet
    B. and
    C. so

13. Certain options may be available on all models. Other options may be available only on the more expensive models.
    A. so
    B. nor (may they be)
    C. but

14. You cannot necessarily pick out all the options for your new vehicle. You should always ask about your choices.
    A. so
    B. nor (should you always ask)
    C. or

15. Your experience buying a vehicle can be pleasant. First, you should do your homework.
    A. but
    B. or
    C. for

Exercise B

Each of the following examples contains two simple sentences that could be combined with a coordinating conjunction. In each case, choose which coordinating conjunction best combines the two sentences (A, B, or C).

1. Hurricane season closed on November 30. A hurricane formed in the ocean on December 2.
    A. yet
    B. so
    C. nor

2. Ray wanted to tape the reality show. He set his VCR before leaving for class.
    A. but
    B. so
    C. nor

3. Kevin and Brian wanted to order pizza. They called the closest pizza place for a delivery.
    A. for
    B. so
    C. or

4. Beverly drank her orange juice. Orange juice is a good source of Vitamin C.
    A. and
    B. yet
    C. for

5. Simone ran into her friend Margie. They didn't have time to chat.
    A. so
    B. for
    C. but

6. Stuck in a boring job, Cedric wanted a better one. He went back to college for more training.
    A. but
    B. so
    C. for

7. The college course was challenging. Barb had to study hard to get a good grade.
    A. yet
    B. so
    C. for

8. The flowered pillow sat on the couch. He wanted it on his chair.
    A. nor (did he want)
    B. for
    C. but

9. Joann cut out the square. She added it to the quilt.
    A. but
    B. and
    C. or

10. Snow continued to fall. Plows were quickly able to clear the roads.
     A. so
     B. nor (were the plows able)
     C. yet

11. The family did not gather at the table for meals. They did not go on any vacations together.
     A. so
     B. nor (did they go)
     C. but

12. Sue did not know exactly where to put the couch. Don and Mike had to keep moving it.
     A. for
     B. yet
     C. so

13. Mario loved Chinese food. He could not eat it every day.
     A. yet
     B. for
     C. so

14. Anxious for something to do, Grandma dusted her end tables. She dusted the lamp shades.
     A. and
     B. for
     C. but

15. Jane wired the new outlet. The family needed another lamp in the family room.
     A. for
     B. and
     C. but

Exercise C

Each of the following examples contains two sentences that could be combined with an adverbial conjunction. In each case, choose which adverbial conjunction best combines the two sentences (A, B, or C).

1. My birthday was last week. It wasn't a good day.
   A. thus
   B. meanwhile
   C. however

2. I woke up late. I missed my first class.
   A. otherwise
   B. therefore
   C. however

3. I had promised to take notes for a friend in that class. He is now mad at me.
   A. meanwhile
   B. consequently
   C. instead

4. We had a pop quiz in math class. In history, I didn't know any answers to the teacher's review questions.
   A. instead
   B. otherwise
   C. furthermore

5. I did get to see my girlfriend at lunch. I reminded her of my birthday.
   A. however
   B. nonetheless
   C. indeed

6. She didn't wish me a happy birthday. I asked her out to dinner that evening.
   A. nonetheless
   B. otherwise
   C. in addition

7. She agreed to have dinner with me. She had to work until six.
   A. in addition
   B. however
   C. thus

8. I was looking forward to dinner. I could hardly wait for 6:30 to come.
   A. indeed
   B. nonetheless
   C. however

9. At 6:30 I picked her up at her apartment. I brought flowers.
   A. thus
   B. otherwise
   C. furthermore

10. She hadn't had much time to prepare. She was beautiful.
    A. consequently
    B. otherwise
    C. nonetheless

11. She gave me a present. It was a very large package.
    A. meanwhile
    B. however
    C. in fact

12. I wanted to open it right then. I waited until after dinner.
    A. instead
    B. thus
    C. consequently

13. We went to Armando's and had a great dinner. The present sat on the empty chair at the table.
    A. thus
    B. meanwhile
    C. indeed

14. Waiters eyed the package with interest. My expectations were growing.
    A. consequently
    B. however
    C. instead

15. It was not the leather coat of my dreams. It was a sweater several sizes too big.
    A. otherwise
    B. consequently
    C. instead

Exercise D

Each of the following examples contains two sentences that could be combined with an adverbial conjunction. In each case, choose which adverbial conjunction best combines the two sentences (A, B, or C).

1. Wool fibers can be made into warm, soft, and strong yarn. The cloth from the yarn is highly valued by the industry and its consumers.
    A. however
    B. hence
    C. instead

2. Wool fibers are curly and crimped. They can be made into a warmer cloth than those from most other fibers.
    A. therefore
    B. instead
    C. otherwise

3. Wool's great warmth results from its fine and curly texture. The curlier the fiber, the more warmth and fluffiness the cloth will have.
    A. besides
    B. however
    C. consequently

4. Curly texture creates tiny pockets of air between the individual fibers. Cold wind cannot easily penetrate the cloth.
    A. hence
    B. besides
    C. in addition

5. A protective barrier of dry air forms next to the body. Comfortable body temperature can be maintained.
    A. therefore
    B. however
    C. otherwise

6. Wool offers the wearer great warmth. The elasticity of wool fibers adds strength and durability.
    A. however
    B. in addition
    C. nonetheless

7. Not all fibers can withstand a forceful pulling. After being pulled, wool fibers spring back to their original shape.
    A. otherwise
    B. therefore
    C. however

8. Animals other than sheep can provide special fibers. These fibers are also collected and woven into yarn.
    A. however
    B. consequently
    C. besides

9. The hair from the Angora goat, called mohair, is the most widely used specialty fiber. Not all areas can provide a suitable climate for raising these animals.
    A. in addition
    B. otherwise
    C. however

10. Hair of the Angora goat grows long and heavy. These goats are sheared twice a year.
    A. consequently
    B. instead
    C. otherwise

11. The cashmere goat's undercoat is exceptionally fine and downy. These more luxurious fibers are much more difficult to obtain.
    A. thus
    B. however
    C. besides

12. Cashmere goats are not sheared. Their fibers are gathered by hand when the goat sheds in spring.
    A. besides
    B. otherwise
    C. instead

13. Each cashmere goat usually yields only four or five ounces of fibers a year. Cashmere items can be quite expensive.
    A. consequently
    B. also
    C. instead

14. The exquisite beauty of a cashmere sweater is in its softness. It is also quite warm.
    A. instead
    B. in addition
    C. therefore

15. Wool's overall resiliency makes it a favorite choice for clothing and blankets. Wool's beautiful dyed colors make it highly valued in fine rugs and decorative tapestries.
    A. thus
    B. furthermore
    C. therefore

Exercise E

Combine the following pairs of sentences using a coordinating conjunction.

1. The food was delicious.
    The music was soft and romantic.

    _____

    _____

2. The earrings were of base metal.
    The other jewelry was 14K gold.

    _____

    _____

3. Barney made reservations at the local steak house.
    He had his future mother-in-law to impress.

    _____

    _____

4. Friday is my favorite day of the week.
    I always go out to dinner and a movie.

    _____

    _____

5. The professional photographer took pictures.
    The relatives took pictures.

    _____

    _____

Exercise F

Combine the following sentences using an adverbial conjunction.

1. The box was not in the trunk.
   It was not on the back seat.

   _____

   _____

2. Maria's brother did not sleep.
   He was grumpy the next morning.

   _____

   _____

3. Scott went to Costa Rica.
   He wanted to surf in a new place.

   _____

   _____

4. Laddie, our dog, is a German shepherd.
   Mittens, our cat, is a Siamese.

   _____

   _____

5. Jeremy might go to the football game.
   He might stay home.

   _____

   _____

Exercise G

The following passage has five errors in punctuating sentences using coordination. Find the errors and correct them using an appropriate option for coordination.

In the Arizona desert, the Saguaro cactus is a unique plant nevertheless it is being maimed and stolen. Not only is the Saguaro the largest species of cactus in the United States but it also takes hundreds of years to grow. Believe it or not, every week people use the Saguaro as target practice. Perhaps these gunmen don't realize the damage they are causing or even worse perhaps they don't care. One bullet can stop decades of growing. Another problem is the theft of these cacti. It is very desirable to have a big Saguaro with its many arms in a yard in Arizona consequently many people dig them up and sell them to homeowners. These gunmen and poachers must be stopped, otherwise these beautiful symbols of the Wild West will disappear from the landscape.

Exercise H

The following passage has five errors in punctuating sentences using coordination. Find the errors and correct them using an appropriate option for coordination.

Some artists use paint or clay to create their art, instead Arthur S. Mole used people. He created group photographs however you could not see the individual people. He arranged tens of thousands of people with different colored shirts, the effect was a patriotic American image. Back when he worked, around 1918, patriotism was very popular. World War I had just ended and people wanted to express their enthusiasm for winning the war. Mole would organize troops into formations like a portrait of Woodrow Wilson, a U.S. shield, the Statue of Liberty, or the Liberty Bell. President Woodrow Wilson was impressed with the photograph of his portrait indeed he signed it with a flourish.

Mastery Test

Each of the following sentences contains a blank. In each case, choose which adverbial conjunction best combines the two clauses (A, B, or C).

1. Caution is the best way to avoid crime; _____, it will not go away completely.
    A. furthermore
    B. in addition
    C. however

2. The demolition team began its work; _____, the building was soon a pile of rubble.
    A. thus
    B. however
    C. moreover

3. The hotel we stayed in was expensive; _____, we had little money for souvenirs.
    A. instead
    B. consequently
    C. similarly

4. Denise and Shelby shopped all day at the mall; _____, they would have been at the game.
    A. otherwise
    B. however
    C. likewise

5. There are scissors in the sewing box; _____, they are fairly new.
    A. besides
    B. nevertheless
    C. indeed

Each of the following pairs of sentences could be combined with a coordinating conjunction. In each case, choose which coordinating conjunction best combines the sentences (A, B, or C).

6. Basketball is my favorite sport to watch on television. I do not like watching football on television.
    A. for
    B. so
    C. but

7. This is an easy test. The test yesterday was easy too.
    A. so
    B. or
    C. and

8. The coordinating conjunctions are easy to remember. The adverbial conjunctions are harder.
    A. but
    B. nor
    C. and

9. I could have fried chicken for lunch. I could have a sandwich.
    A. so
    B. and
    C. or

10. The day was cloudy. We expected rain.
    A. so
    B. but
    C. and

Combining Sentences Using Subordination

Diagnostic Test

For questions 1–4, choose the answer (A or B) that correctly identifies each group of words. Is it a dependent clause or an independent clause?

1. if you decide to come
   A. dependent clause
   B. independent clause

2. luckily, you decided to come
   A. dependent clause
   B. independent clause

3. before the class began
   A. dependent clause
   B. independent clause

4. unless he calls tonight
   A. dependent clause
   B. independent clause

For questions 5–7, select which of the following answers (A, B, or C) is a correct example of subordination.

5. A. The boy tried to catch the dog, whenever he saw it.
   B. Whenever the boy saw the dog he tried to catch it.
   C. Whenever the boy saw the dog, he tried to catch it.

6. A. Video games are not any fun unless there is plenty of adventure.
   B. Unless there is plenty of adventure video games are not any fun.
   C. Video games are not any fun, unless there is plenty of adventure.

7. A. Surfing is a wonderful exercise but it is hard on your arms and legs.
   B. Surfing is a wonderful exercise, although it is hard on your arms and legs.
   C. Although surfing is a wonderful exercise, it is hard on your arms and legs.

For questions 8–10, combine the two sentences into one using the given relative pronoun.

8. Jayne is in my next class.
   I am eating lunch with her.
   (whom)

_____

_____

9. The French horn is an antique.
   Zanetta plays the French horn.
   (that)

   _____

   _____

10. My doctor will be on vacation next week.
    His office is decorated with a jungle motif.
    (whose)

    _____

    _____

Exercise A

Choose the answer (A or B) that correctly identifies each group of words. Is it a dependent clause or an independent clause?

1. more Americans are reconsidering the more traditional views on medicine and healing
   A. dependent clause
   B. independent clause

2. herbal remedies have recently gained closer attention
   A. dependent clause
   B. independent clause

3. since an appreciation for the "natural" has increased
   A. dependent clause
   B. independent clause

4. herbals have become an alternative growing in popularity
   A. dependent clause
   B. independent clause

5. if herbals become more popular than traditional pharmaceutical drugs
   A. dependent clause
   B. independent clause

6. herbal remedies are appealing to consumers with holistic health beliefs
   A. dependent clause
   B. independent clause

7. although the rising costs and reports of ineffectiveness are worrisome
   A. dependent clause
   B. independent clause

8. debilitating side effects to many pharmaceuticals have brought about interest in possible alternatives
   A. dependent clause
   B. independent clause

9. many are researching and experimenting with herbs
   A. dependent clause
   B. independent clause

10. because many are willing to risk side effects of pharmaceuticals
    A. dependent clause
    B. independent clause

11. others are willing to rely on a more "natural cure" for the body
    A. dependent clause
    B. independent clause

12. many consumers are heading to the herbalist
    A. dependent clause
    B. independent clause

13. while the cost of conventional healthcare is rising
    A. dependent clause
    B. independent clause

14. scientific information about the safety of herbal remedies is often not available
    A. dependent clause
    B. independent clause

15. this leaves the entire subject wide open for vast avenues of research
    A. dependent clause
    B. independent clause

Exercise B

Choose the answer (A or B) that correctly identifies each group of words. Is it a dependent clause or an independent clause?

1. as the incidence of clinical depression has risen
    A. dependent clause
    B. independent clause

2. many sufferers are seeking relief from St. John's wort
    A. dependent clause
    B. independent clause

3. which is used primarily as an antidepressant
    A. dependent clause
    B. independent clause

4. treatments for depression are numerous
    A. dependent clause
    B. independent clause

5. traditional pharmaceutical antidepressants are the drugs of choice
    A. dependent clause
    B. independent clause

6. when Prozac, Zoloft, and Paxil became household names
    A. dependent clause
    B. independent clause

7. these drugs have been proven to be effective
    A. dependent clause
    B. independent clause

8. although the high cost and controversy over side effects invite consideration
    A. dependent clause
    B. independent clause

9. many pharmaceutical antidepressants must be taken for weeks
    A. dependent clause
    B. independent clause

10. before significant results can be felt
    A. dependent clause
    B. independent clause

11. trying an herbal remedy like St. John's wort can be another option worthy of consideration
    A. dependent clause
    B. independent clause

12. oftentimes they prove to be far less costly
    A. dependent clause
    B. independent clause

13. questions remain unanswered
    A. dependent clause
    B. independent clause

14. studies continue to reveal answers
    A. dependent clause
    B. independent clause

15. that add to the controversy between herbals and pharmaceuticals
    A. dependent clause
    B. independent clause

Exercise C

Choose the answer (A, B, or C) that shows a sentence in which either the subordinating conjunction or relative pronoun is appropriate to the meaning.

1.   A.   I am an independent person after I sometimes need my parents.
     B.   I am an independent person although I sometimes need my parents.
     C.   I am an independent person before I sometimes need my parents.

2.   A.   Sam, whose real name is Samantha, is a beautiful and talented woman.
     B.   Sam, which real name is Samantha, is a beautiful and talented woman.
     C.   Sam, that real name is Samantha, is a beautiful and talented woman.

3.   A.   Frank, who used to be a firefighter, is a part-time clown now.
     B.   Frank, whom used to be a firefighter, is a part-time clown now.
     C.   Frank, which used to be a firefighter, is a part-time clown now.

4.   A.   Ohio became a state unless Indiana became a state.
     B.   Ohio became a state although Indiana became a state.
     C.   Ohio became a state before Indiana became a state.

5.   A.   After a difficult pregnancy, the cow whom was out in the pasture was ready to have its calf.
     B.   After a difficult pregnancy, the cow that was out in the pasture was ready to have its calf.
     C.   After a difficult pregnancy, the cow whose was out in the pasture was ready to have its calf.

6.   A.   Since Sally does not have a job this semester, she will need financial aid.
     B.   Even though Sally does not have a job this semester, she will need financial aid.
     C.   Where Sally does not have a job this semester, she will need financial aid.

7.   A.   George got a remote control who could control all of his electronic devices.
     B.   George got a remote control that could control all of his electronic devices.
     C.   George got a remote control because could control all of his electronic devices.

8.   A.   If Alex became a baseball player for a semi-professional team, Rachel got to travel to Pasadena, California, for a game.
     B.   Where Alex became a baseball player for a semi-professional team, Rachel got to travel to Pasadena, California, for a game.
     C.   Because Alex became a baseball player for a semi-professional team, Rachel got to travel to Pasadena, California, for a game.

9.   A.   Unless Becky gets a passing grade on the test, she will not pass math this semester.
     B.   Because Becky gets a passing grade on the test, she will not pass math this semester.
     C.   As if Becky gets a passing grade on the test, she will not pass math this semester.

10. A.   In the garden, Cecil planted roses and tomatoes because he wanted beauty and food.
     B.   In the garden, Cecil planted roses and tomatoes if he wanted beauty and food.
     C.   In the garden, Cecil planted roses and tomatoes whether he wanted beauty and food.

Exercise D

Choose the answer (A, B, or C) that shows a sentence in which either the subordinating conjunction or relative pronoun is appropriate to the meaning.

1.   A.   Three small words, declared by Neil Armstrong, whose voice surged from Houston to the whole world, began one of mankind's greatest stories.
     B.   Three small words, declared by Neil Armstrong, which voice surged from Houston to the whole world, began one of mankind's greatest stories.
     C.   Three small words, declared by Neil Armstrong, who voice surged from Houston to the whole world, began one of mankind's greatest stories.

2.   A.   The brave pioneers were Neil Armstrong and Edwin Aldrin, and the date was July 20, 1969, a date whose would bridge a vast gap.
     B.   The brave pioneers were Neil Armstrong and Edwin Aldrin, and the date was July 20, 1969, a date whom would bridge a vast gap.
     C.   The brave pioneers were Neil Armstrong and Edwin Aldrin, and the date was July 20, 1969, a date which would bridge a vast gap.

3.   A.   The last moments, which must have seemed suspended at the time, led to sighs of relief.
     B.   The last moments, since must have seemed suspended at the time, led to sighs of relief.
     C.   The last moments, when must have seemed suspended at the time, led to sighs of relief.

4.   A.   "The eagle has landed," was the declaration, whom will ring forever in history.
     B.   "The eagle has landed," was the declaration, which will ring forever in history.
     C.   "The eagle has landed," was the declaration, who will ring forever in history.

5.   A.   Man had reached the moon; it was a dream that had held many for centuries.
     B.   Man had reached the moon; it was a dream whom had held many for centuries.
     C.   Man had reached the moon; it was a dream whose had held many for centuries.

6.   A.   If Armstrong's words, "That's one small step for man, one giant leap for mankind," will surely be remembered, those first four words somehow more accurately defined the moment.
     B.   Although Armstrong's words, "That's one small step for man, one giant leap for mankind," will surely be remembered, those first four words somehow more accurately defined the moment.
     C.   Unless Armstrong's words, "That's one small step for man, one giant leap for mankind," will surely be remembered, those first four words somehow more accurately defined the moment.

7.   A.   The other significant moment was when the two were again ready to blast away from the moon into the lunar orbit as though the third crew member was orbiting in the command module.
     B.   The other significant moment was when the two were again ready to blast away from the moon into the lunar orbit although the third crew member was orbiting in the command module.
     C.   The other significant moment was when the two were again ready to blast away from the moon into the lunar orbit where the third crew member was orbiting in the command module.

© 2005 Thomson Wadsworth

8. A. If the single ascent engine had failed, Neil Armstrong, "Buzz" Aldrin, and Michael Collins would never have become the American heroes they are.
    B. While the single ascent engine had failed, Neil Armstrong, "Buzz" Aldrin, and Michael Collins would never have become the American heroes they are.
    C. Unless the single ascent engine had failed, Neil Armstrong, "Buzz" Aldrin, and Michael Collins would never have become the American heroes they are.

9. A. Lunar observers, who have widely studied the moon, can now be quite certain that there have never been any life forms on the moon.
    B. Lunar observers, whom have widely studied the moon, can now be quite certain that there have never been any life forms on the moon.
    C. Lunar observers, which have widely studied the moon, can now be quite certain that there have never been any life forms on the moon.

10. A. It is probably safe to bet that lunar observation, as well as space travel, will continue when the end of our time.
    B. It is probably safe to bet that lunar observation, as well as space travel, will continue until the end of our time.
    C. It is probably safe to bet that lunar observation, as well as space travel, will continue where the end of our time.

Exercise E

For questions 1–5, combine the following pairs of sentences using a subordinating conjunction to make the meaning clear. Choose from the following: *after, although, as, because, before, even though, if, provided that, since, until, unless, when, wherever.*

1. Tropical plants will not flourish.
    You provide them with water, nutrients, and light.

    _____

    _____

2. Tropical plants grow naturally in warmer climates.
    People in colder places can enjoy them indoors during the autumn and winter months.

    _____

    _____

3. Tropical plants are kept under ideal conditions.
    Some species will even flower, adding to their beauty.

    _____

    _____

4. They are taken inside before the first cold air of autumn comes.
    Tropical plants can be put outside for an extra boost.

    _____

    _____

5. They are placed in the home.
    Tropical plants add beautiful color and texture.

    _____

    _____

For questions 6–10, use a relative pronoun to combine the pair of sentences. Choose from the following: *who, whose, whom, which,* or *that.*

6. The concert hall is filled to capacity.
    It has now grown silent.

    _____

    _____

7. That violinist is the concertmaster.
   He is the youngest orchestra member.

   _____

   _____

8. The older members have great respect for him.
   They await his entrance.

   _____

   _____

9. The young concertmaster is a favorite among Philadelphia audiences.
   His artistry is matched by his graciousness.

   _____

   _____

10. The young man's mother has come to see her son's debut.
    She lives in Chicago.

    _____

    _____

Exercise F

For questions 1–5, use subordination to combine each pair of sentences. Be careful to use a subordinating conjunction that is appropriate to the meaning.

1.   We went to London.
      We wanted to see Big Ben.

      _____

      _____

2.   Orlando agreed to go on the trip.
      He could visit his friend afterwards.

      _____

      _____

3.   His charisma carried him through the presentation.
      He didn't know much about the topic.

      _____

      _____

4.   My aunt moved away.
      Life hasn't been the same.

      _____

      _____

5.   Shirley wants to drive.
      We can go into the city tonight.

      _____

      _____

For questions 6–10, use subordination to combine each pair of sentences. Be careful to use an appropriate relative pronoun.

6.   The garden was a perfect retreat.
      The trees blocked the hot midday sun.

      _____

      _____

7.   Good soil must be created.
     Good soil is hard to find in this area.

     _____

     _____

8.   Frank Lloyd Wright was a noted architect.
     Frank Lloyd Wright designed the Guggenheim Museum.

     _____

     _____

9.   The Atlanta Botanical Garden is a volunteer-run garden.
     It is located on Piedmont Avenue.

     _____

     _____

10. The title of Hemingway's *For Whom the Bell Tolls* comes from the poem, "No Man Is an
     Island."
     The author of the poem, "No Man Is an Island" is John Donne.

     _____

     _____

Exercise G

The following passage is written using simple sentences. Rewrite the passage, using subordination to combine sentences in at least three places.

John was sleeping beneath the warm army blanket. The radio alarm cut in with the morning weather and travel advisory. The storm had arrived just as predicted. John jumped up from his warm covers. The room was cold. He is like many other road workers. He secretly enjoys the challenge of a snowstorm. Bed is warm and comfortable. John's sense of duty is greater. In the predawn, snowdrifts cover the city streets. Without plowing, morning traffic would be at a standstill. John and the rest of the snow removal crew arrive with giant plows. The plows push the snow to the sides. Intersections are sanded or covered with rock salt. Few commuters will be troubled. They start off for work at 8:00 AM.

_____

_____

_____

_____

_____

_____

_____

_____

_____

_____

_____

_____

Exercise H

Combine the simple sentences in each of the following questions by using subordinating conjuctions and/or relative pronouns.

1. Bob Hope was in vaudeville, radio, and movies.
    He died in 2003.
    He was 100 years old.

    _____

    _____

    _____

2. Hope was born in 1903 in England.
    He moved to Cleveland, Ohio.
    He was four years old.

    _____

    _____

    _____

3. Hope changed his name.
    He was originally Leslie Townes Hope.
    He became an entertainer.

    _____

    _____

    _____

4. Bob Hope appeared in over 70 movies.
    He is most famous for performing in hundreds of USO programs.
    He started these shows during World War II.

    _____

    _____

    _____

5. Hope performed in Europe, Japan, South Korea, Vietnam, and the Persian Gulf.
    Hope was named an honorary military veteran in 1997 by President Clinton.

    _____

    _____

    _____

6.   Kelsey Grammar hosted a television special honoring Hope on his 100th birthday. Kelsey Grammar is one of Hope's biggest fans.

_____

_____

_____

Exercise I

Below are sentences with restrictive and nonrestrictive clauses. For each pair, choose the sentence (A or B) that has the correct punctuation.

1. A. Her laughter, which was rich and hearty, surprised the courtroom.
    B. Her laughter which was rich and hearty surprised the courtroom.

2. A. I couldn't put down the newspaper, that carried the story.
    B. I couldn't put down the newspaper that carried the story.

3. A. The girl, who is wearing the black dress, is one of the witnesses.
    B. The girl who is wearing the black dress is one of the witnesses.

4. A. Security guards, who were placed at every doorway, quickly showed us to our places.
    B. Security guards who were placed at every doorway quickly showed us to our places.

5. A. That lawyer has penetrating eyes, that look right through you.
    B. That lawyer has penetrating eyes that look right through you.

6. A. The case, which is very controversial, is being tried here in Dade County.
    B. The case which is very controversial is being tried here in Dade County.

7. A. One piece of evidence that is crucial remains under lock and key.
    B. One piece of evidence, that is crucial, remains under lock and key.

8. A. The most important witness, whose testimony is suspect, is under protective surveillance.
    B. The most important witness whose testimony is suspect is under protective surveillance.

9. A. Judge Hodges, who presides over this case, must keep order in the court.
    B. Judge Hodges who presides over this case must keep order in the court.

10. A. The facts of this case, which might surprise the public, are yet to be disclosed.
    B. The facts of this case which might surprise the public are yet to be disclosed.

Mastery Test

Each of the following sentences contains a blank. Choose the answer (A, B, or C) that shows the correct subordinating conjunction to use for the sentence to make sense.

1. _____ broccoli florets can be enjoyed raw with light seasoning in a salad, they can also be sautéed in olive oil and garlic.
    A. Because
    B. Although
    C. Since

2. Broccoli can be a delicious crunchy snack _____ the dark green or purple florets are tightly closed.
    A. provided that
    B. unless
    C. when

3. Spinach is an extremely versatile vegetable that is very nutritious _____ washing and de-stemming the leaves is quite a chore.
    A. while
    B. even though
    C. until

4. When buying Brussels sprouts, choose bright green heads which are round and firm _____ these qualities indicate peak freshness.
    A. although
    B. unless
    C. because

5. _____ you choose broccoli, spinach, or Brussels sprouts, including a green vegetable can complement beef, pork, fish, or fowl.
    A. Before
    B. Whether
    C. After

Each of the following sentences contains a blank. Choose the answer (A, B, or C) that shows the correct relative pronoun to use for the sentence to make sense.

6. My friend Mona, _____ house is just across the fence, has a big herb garden.
    A. whom
    B. who
    C. whose

7. Her biggest crop is basil, both green and purple, _____ grows in the center of all the other herbs.
    A. whom
    B. who
    C. which

8. Mona, from _____ I have learned so much about seeding and growing, has sparked my own interest in gardening.
   A. whom
   B. who
   C. whose

9. However, it is really my husband, _____, I believe, gave me my first introduction to the grand art of gardening and harvesting one's own herbs and vegetables.
   A. whom
   B. who
   C. whose

10. Mark, _____ rosemary grew into the size of shrubs, has the "greenest" of thumbs!
    A. whom
    B. who
    C. whose

Correcting Fragments and Run-Ons

Diagnostic Test

For questions 1–5, identify each example as (A) a fragment, (B) a run-on, or (C) a complete sentence.

1. I walked around to the side of the house the gate was open.
    A. fragment
    B. run-on
    C. complete sentence

2. In the back of the yard, where the larger rocks naturally form a small mountainside.
    A. fragment
    B. run-on
    C. complete sentence

3. When the delicate purple flowers bloom between the stones.
    A. fragment
    B. run-on
    C. complete sentence

4. I nodded happily, then I leaned back against a large rock.
    A. fragment
    B. run-on
    C. complete sentence

5. After all these years, I have found a new friend.
    A. fragment
    B. run-on
    C. complete sentence

For questions 6–10, each example is a fragment or a run-on. Rewrite each example as a complete sentence.

6. Mr. Nye has spent most of his adult life trying to save bald eagles from extinction and he has nursed hundreds of eaglets.

    _____

    _____

    _____

7. The man in charge of one of the most successful reintroduction programs in the country.

    _____

    _____

    _____

8. Eagles have been seen this past winter on ice floes in the Hudson River near the George Washington Bridge, furthermore one Audubon member reported seeing an eagle flying over Grant's Tomb.

_____

_____

_____

9. Mr. Nye started in the 1970s, the bald eagle was a rare sight.

_____

_____

_____

10. In 1970, there was only one known nesting pair of eagles in New York State but today there are 75 pairs.

_____

_____

_____

Exercise A

Identify each of the following groups of words as (A) a phrase or (B) a clause.

1. unless the volunteers make an extra effort
    A. phrase
    B. clause

2. during the decade
    A. phrase
    B. clause

3. after the ceremony
    A. phrase
    B. clause

4. after the money was counted
    A. phrase
    B. clause

5. if nothing more is done
    A. phrase
    B. clause

6. to see the ending
    A. phrase
    B. clause

7. walking the narrow path
    A. phrase
    B. clause

8. while they were walking
    A. phrase
    B. clause

9. whenever the vote is taken
    A. phrase
    B. clause

10. have never been surprised
    A. phrase
    B. clause

Exercise B

Identify each of the following groups of words as (A) a phrase or (B) a clause.

1.   among the other jazz bands
      A.   phrase
      B.   clause

2.   rehearsing for dances and using simple musical devices
      A.   phrase
      B.   clause

3.   which are basically grouped into categories
      A.   phrase
      B.   clause

4.   with his usual tenor saxophone improvisations
      A.   phrase
      B.   clause

5.   as she belted out a familiar tune
      A.   phrase
      B.   clause

6.   under the direction of Count Basie
      A.   phrase
      B.   clause

7.   when the band played the last few songs
      A.   phrase
      B.   clause

8.   playing under difficult circumstances
      A.   phrase
      B.   clause

9.   who performed last week in New Orleans
      A.   phrase
      B.   clause

10.   with a crisp, powerful brass section
      A.   phrase
      B.   clause

Exercise C

For each of the following examples, choose the answer (A, B, or C) that correctly identifies the example as a fragment, a run-on, or a complete sentence.

1. When Daniel Wallace set out to write his novel *Big Fish*.
    A. fragment
    B. run-on
    C. complete sentence

2. He did not realize that his novel was about his own father.
    A. fragment
    B. run-on
    C. complete sentence

3. The main character is Edward Bloom, a liar, an adulterer, and a weaver of tall tales.
    A. fragment
    B. run-on
    C. complete sentence

4. As he lies dying.
    A. fragment
    B. run-on
    C. complete sentence

5. His son tries to understand him and forgive him.
    A. fragment
    B. run-on
    C. complete sentence

6. Edward Bloom could be so charming he could sell you anything.
    A. fragment
    B. run-on
    C. complete sentence

7. He also had a dark side, he told lies and was often absent.
    A. fragment
    B. run-on
    C. complete sentence

8. In the book, the father's tall tales take on mythic proportions.
    A. fragment
    B. run-on
    C. complete sentence

9. Watching the film version of his book, Wallace was uncomfortable at first however after the fourth viewing he liked it.
    A. fragment
    B. run-on
    C. complete sentence

10. Knowing that his relationship with his father had been mostly by phone.
    A. fragment
    B. run-on
    C. complete sentence

Exercise D

For each of the following examples, choose the answer (A, B, or C) that correctly identifies the example as a fragment, a run-on, or a complete sentence.

1. The nervous system is composed of countless nerve cells, which are the basic units of this complex system.
   A. fragment
   B. run-on
   C. complete sentence

2. Nerve cells are called neurons, they are present all throughout the body.
   A. fragment
   B. run-on
   C. complete sentence

3. Neuroglia, acting as a supportive framework around them.
   A. fragment
   B. run-on
   C. complete sentence

4. Signals are sent to the brain via the neurons and these signals travel from neuron to neuron.
   A. fragment
   B. run-on
   C. complete sentence

5. A synapse is the junction between neurons.
   A. fragment
   B. run-on
   C. complete sentence

6. After the brain interprets these signals.
   A. fragment
   B. run-on
   C. complete sentence

7. Messages are sent back through other nerve cells.
   A. fragment
   B. run-on
   C. complete sentence

8. These messages can order movement, they can bring muscles into action.
   A. fragment
   B. run-on
   C. complete sentence

9. It is no wonder the complex arrangement of neurons has been a crucial subject of exploration for brain researchers.
   A. fragment
   B. run-on
   C. complete sentence

10. The brain is the master of the nervous system, it is the commander of all the body's other systems.
    A. fragment
    B. run-on
    C. complete sentence

11. With some of the primary parts being the cerebrum, the cerebellum, the thalamus, the hypothalamus, and the brain stem.
    A. fragment
    B. run-on
    C. complete sentence

12. Each part has a distinct function.
    A. fragment
    B. run-on
    C. complete sentence

13. The spinal cord connects to the brain at the brain stem.
    A. fragment
    B. run-on
    C. complete sentence

14. The spinal cord, also composed of neurons and neuroglia, acts as a communication pathway.
    A. fragment
    B. run-on
    C. complete sentence

15. The brain and the spinal cord work together, they both comprise the central nervous system.
    A. fragment
    B. run-on
    C. complete sentence

Exercise E

Choose the answer (A, B, or C) that correctly identifies each group of words as a fragment, a run-on, or a complete sentence.

1. The autonomic nervous system, which regulates major organs.
    A. fragment
    B. run-on sentence
    C. complete sentence

2. The top of the spinal cord, connecting with the brain at the brain stem, begins to thicken.
    A. fragment
    B. run-on sentence
    C. complete sentence

3. Known as the medulla, has nerves that connect to the face.
    A. fragment
    B. run-on sentence
    C. complete sentence

4. Many of the body's reflexes make connections through the medulla.
    A. fragment
    B. run-on sentence
    C. complete sentence

5. Such a basic function as coughing.
    A. fragment
    B. run-on sentence
    C. complete sentence

6. The medulla also controls other reflexes that are unconscious, an example is the moving of food through the digestive system through peristalsis.
    A. fragment
    B. run-on sentence
    C. complete sentence

7. Which breaks up food and moves it through the intestines.
    A. fragment
    B. run-on sentence
    C. complete sentence

8. The vital activities of the body—the beating of the heart and the rhythmic movement of the lungs—are also reliant on the medulla.
    A. fragment
    B. run-on sentence
    C. complete sentence

9. Major motor nerves cross at the medulla, nerves on the left side go to the right brain and nerves on the right side go to the left brain.
    A. fragment
    B. run-on sentence
    C. complete sentence

10. With its many synapses, carries messages back and forth between cerebrum and muscles.
    A. fragment
    B. run-on sentence
    C. complete sentence

11. The pons lies just above the medulla it connects the medulla to the cerebrum.
    A. fragment
    B. run-on sentence
    C. complete sentence

12. The midbrain, which assists in muscle control.
    A. fragment
    B. run-on sentence
    C. complete sentence

13. Relaying messages about hot and cold.
    A. fragment
    B. run-on sentence
    C. complete sentence

14. Below the thalamus, the hypothalamus controls the amount of water in the body.
    A. fragment
    B. run-on sentence
    C. complete sentence

15. In the hypothalamus, the body's appetite and resulting hunger are regulated, this is a crucial factor in sustaining optimal bodily function.
    A. fragment
    B. run-on sentence
    C. complete sentence

Exercise F

Choose the sentence (A, B, or C) that is not a run-on sentence.

1.   A.   Someone has written on the overhead projector; the writing is in permanent marker.
     B.   Someone has written on the overhead projector and the writing is in permanent marker.
     C.   Someone has written on the overhead projector, the writing is in permanent marker.

2.   A.   Colorful posters adorn the campus with messages of student success but they are being replaced with cheaper versions.
     B.   Colorful posters adorn the campus with messages of student success they are being replaced with cheaper versions.
     C.   Colorful posters adorn the campus with messages of student success, but they are being replaced with cheaper versions.

3.   A.   Mel wanted to be a pilot, therefore he began lessons at the airport.
     B.   Mel wanted to be a pilot; therefore, he began lessons at the airport.
     C.   Mel wanted to be a pilot; therefore he began lessons at the airport.

4.   A.   That podium is broken do not use it.
     B.   That podium is broken, do not use it.
     C.   That podium is broken, so do not use it.

5.   A.   The young man was late for the exam; therefore, the proctor would not allow him into the room.
     B.   The young man was late for the exam, therefore, the proctor would not allow him into the room.
     C.   The young man was late for the exam therefore the proctor would not allow him into the room.

6.   A.   I love to read, nevertheless I have not read a good novel in a while.
     B.   I love to read; nevertheless I have not read a good novel in a while.
     C.   I love to read; nevertheless, I have not read a good novel in a while.

7.   A.   When Danielle joined the chorus; she wanted Greg to join, too.
     B.   When Danielle joined the chorus, she wanted Greg to join, too.
     C.   Danielle joined the chorus, she wanted Greg to join, too.

8.   A.   Don had a purple sedan, yet his dream car was a convertible.
     B.   Don had a purple sedan yet his dream car was a convertible.
     C.   Don had a purple sedan, his dream car was a convertible.

9.   A.   Even though the students worked diligently on their essays they did not proofread carefully.
     B.   Even though the students worked diligently on their essays, they did not proofread carefully.
     C.   Even though the students worked diligently on their essays; they did not proofread carefully.

10. A.   Irene had blond hair however, her brother was a redhead.
     B.   Irene had blond hair; however, her brother was a redhead.
     C.   Irene had blond hair, however; her brother was a redhead.

11. A. Since classes were not in session yet, the teachers did not have to stay the entire day.
    B. Since classes were not in session yet; the teachers did not have to stay the entire day.
    C. Since classes were not in session yet the teachers did not have to stay the entire day.

12. A. Having a balanced diet and getting exercise are ways to getting fit but some people need a support group or at least a friend to exercise with them.
    B. Having a balanced diet and getting exercise are ways to getting fit, but some people need a support group or at least a friend to exercise with them.
    C. Having a balanced diet and getting exercise are ways to getting fit; but some people need a support group or at least a friend to exercise with them.

13. A. The teacher expected that her students already knew basic word processing; therefore, she wanted the students to word process all of their papers.
    B. The teacher expected that her students already knew basic word processing, therefore, she wanted the students to word process all of their papers.
    C. The teacher expected that her students already knew basic word processing therefore she wanted the students to word process all of their papers.

14. A. After Joe had discussed the work problem with his father, he realized that he would have to quit his job.
    B. After Joe had discussed the work problem with his father he realized that he would have to quit his job.
    C. After Joe had discussed the work problem with his father; he realized that he would have to quit his job.

15. A. Jose developed the comic book concept during high school his college art teacher told him to get it published.
    B. Jose developed the comic book concept during high school, his college art teacher told him to get it published.
    C. Jose developed the comic book concept during high school; his college art teacher told him to get it published.

Exercise G

Each of the following examples is a run-on sentence. Choose the answer (A, B, or C) that corrects the run-on.

1. The clothes on the hanger were damp, the clothes in the dryer were wet.
    A. The clothes on the hanger were damp and the clothes in the dryer were wet.
    B. The clothes on the hanger were damp, and the clothes in the dryer were wet.
    C. The clothes on the hanger were damp the clothes in the dryer were wet.

2. Clay was home he was not paying attention to his laundry.
    A. Clay was home, but he was not paying attention to his laundry.
    B. Clay was home, he was not paying attention to his laundry.
    C. Clay was home and he was not paying attention to his laundry.

3. I found Clay in his room, he was playing video games.
    A. I found Clay in his room he was playing video games.
    B. I found Clay in his room and he was playing video games.
    C. When I found Clay in his room, he was playing video games.

4. His favorite game is a car race, sometimes, I play against him.
    A. His favorite game is a car race; I play against him sometimes.
    B. His favorite game is a car race sometimes, I play against him.
    C. His favorite game is a car race, sometimes; I play against him.

5. I am not very fast on the controls, however, I am a better driver than he is.
    A. I am not very fast on the controls; however, I am a better driver than he is.
    B. I am not very fast on the controls however, I am a better driver than he is.
    C. I am not very fast on the controls, however I am a better driver than he is.

6. When I play, I use the yellow car and Clay always chooses the faster red car.
    A. When I play I use the yellow car, and Clay always chooses the faster red car.
    B. When I play, I use the yellow car and, Clay always chooses the faster red car.
    C. When I play, I use the yellow car, and Clay always chooses the faster red car.

7. Unfortunately for him, the faster car does not handle as well on the curves so I have an advantage in my slower car.
    A. Unfortunately for him, the faster car does not handle as well on the curves and so I have an advantage in my slower car.
    B. Unfortunately for him, the faster car does not handle as well on the curves, so I have an advantage in my slower car.
    C. Unfortunately for him, the faster car does not handle as well on the curves; so I have an advantage in my slower car.

8. In this game, the winner is allowed to choose options to add to the car, therefore I add engine power when I win.
    A. In this game, the winner is allowed to choose options to add to the car therefore I add engine power when I win.
    B. In this game, the winner is allowed to choose options to add to the car, therefore, I add engine power when I win.
    C. In this game, the winner is allowed to choose options to add to the car; therefore, I add engine power when I win.

9.   The added engine power gives me a little more speed I sacrifice handling.
     A.   The added engine power gives me a little more speed but I sacrifice handling.
     B.   Although the added engine power gives me a little more speed, I sacrifice handling.
     C.   The added engine power gives me a little more speed, I sacrifice handling.

10. I have added horsepower, however, I always wreck my car in the next race.
     A.   I have added horsepower however I always wreck my car in the next race.
     B.   I have added horsepower, however I always wreck my car in the next race.
     C.   I have added horsepower; however, I always wreck my car in the next race.

Exercise H

Choose the sentence (A, B, or C) that is not a run-on sentence.

1. A. Antarctica is a continent in the Southern Hemisphere, it is home to the South Pole.
    B. Antarctica is a continent in the Southern Hemisphere, and it is home to the South Pole.
    C. Antarctica is a continent in the Southern Hemisphere it is home to the South Pole.

2. A. British, Russian, and American explorers discovered that Antarctica is a continent; it was originally thought to be a series of islands.
    B. British, Russian, and American explorers discovered that Antarctica is a continent it was originally thought to be a series of islands.
    C. British, Russian, and American explorers discovered that Antarctica is a continent, it was originally thought to be a series of islands.

3. A. Antarctica is fourteen million square kilometers wide therefore it is the fifth largest continent.
    B. Antarctica is fourteen million square kilometers wide; therefore, it is the fifth largest continent.
    C. Antarctica is fourteen million square kilometers wide, therefore; it is the fifth largest continent.

4. A. The main port is McMurdo; the main natural resources are iron ore, copper, gold, and platinum.
    B. The main port is McMurdo and the main natural resources are iron ore, copper, gold, and platinum.
    C. The main port is McMurdo, the main natural resources are iron ore, copper, gold, and platinum.

5. A. These natural resources have not been exploited the average temperature is just slightly above freezing.
    B. These natural resources have not been exploited, because the average temperature is just slightly above freezing.
    C. These natural resources have not been exploited because the average temperature is just slightly above freezing.

6. A. The highest temperatures are in January, the Southern Hemisphere has summer when we are having winter.
    B. The highest temperatures are in January; the Southern Hemisphere has summer when we are having winter.
    C. The highest temperatures are in January the Southern Hemisphere has summer when we are having winter.

7. A. No people are from Antarctica, but twenty-seven countries send research personnel there to live.
    B. No people are from Antarctica twenty-seven countries send research personnel there to live.
    C. No people are from Antarctica but twenty-seven countries send research personnel there to live.

8. A. In Antarctica's winter, one thousand people operate research stations while in the summer, up to four thousand people work there.
    B. In Antarctica's winter, one thousand people operate research stations, in the summer, up to four thousand people live there.
    C. In Antarctica's winter, one thousand people operate research stations however in the summer, up to four thousand people work there.

9. A. More solar radiation reaches the South Pole than the equator even though the equator gets much warmer.
    B. More solar radiation reaches the South Pole than the equator the equator gets much warmer.
    C. More solar radiation reaches the South Pole than the equator; even though, the equator gets much warmer.

10. A. Antarctica has 280,000 ice-free square kilometers and nothing can be grown there.
    B. Antarctica has 280,000 ice-free square kilometers, nothing can be grown there.
    C. Antarctica has 280,000 ice-free square kilometers, and nothing can be grown there.

Mastery Test

Each of the following examples is a run-on sentence. Choose the answer (A, B, or C) in which the run-on is revised correctly and makes sense.

1. Marilyn Monroe was born on June 1, 1926 she was born in Los Angeles.
   A. Marilyn Monroe was born on June 1, 1926, she was born in Los Angeles.
   B. Marilyn Monroe was born on June 1, 1926, in Los Angeles.
   C. Marilyn Monroe was born on June 1,1926 and she was born in Los Angeles.

2. Her parents were Gladys and Martin Mortenson but she was educated by many adoptive families.
   A. Her parents were Gladys and Martin Mortenson; however, she was educated by different adoptive families.
   B. Her parents were Gladys and Martin Mortenson; but she was educated by different adoptive families.
   C. Her parents were Gladys and Martin Mortenson, however, she was educated by different adoptive families.

3. Marilyn Monroe first married at 16 and her first husband was James Dougherty.
   A. Marilyn Monroe first married at 16 and, her first husband was James Dougherty.
   B. Marilyn Monroe first married at 16, and her first husband was James Dougherty.
   C. Marilyn Monroe first married at 16, her first husband was James Dougherty.

4. Monroe contracted for seven years with 20th Century Fox, she made 15 films in three years.
   A. Monroe contracted for seven years with 20th Century Fox; she made 15 films in three years.
   B. Monroe contracted for seven years with 20th Century Fox and she made 15 films in three years.
   C. Monroe contracted for seven years with 20th Century Fox she made 15 films in three years.

5. In 1950 she got her first role in *Asphalt Jungle* she played a gangster's wife.
   A. In 1950 she got her first role in *Asphalt Jungle* and she played a gangster's wife.
   B. In 1950 she got her first role in *Asphalt Jungle*; she played a gangster's wife.
   C. In 1950 she got her first role in *Asphalt Jungle*, she played a gangster's wife.

6. She made *Niagara, Gentlemen Prefer Blondes,* and *How to Marry a Millionaire* in 1953, she became an international success.
   A. She made *Niagara, Gentlemen Prefer Blondes,* and *How to Marry a Millionaire* in 1953; consequently, she became an international success.
   B. In 1953 she made *Niagara, Gentlemen Prefer Blondes,* and *How to Marry a Millionaire,* she became an international success.
   C. She made *Niagara, Gentlemen Prefer Blondes,* and *How to Marry a Millionaire* in 1953 she became an international success.

7.   After breaking her contract, Monroe met and collaborated with Milton H. Greene and
     Monroe returned to 20th Century Fox under better working conditions.
     A.   After breaking her contract, Monroe met and collaborated with Milton H. Greene.
          Monroe then returned to 20th Century Fox under better working conditions.
     B.   After breaking her contract, Monroe met and collaborated with Milton H. Greene
          and, Monroe returned to 20th Century Fox under better working conditions.
     C.   After breaking her contract, Monroe met and collaborated with Milton H. Greene,
          Monroe returned to 20th Century Fox under better working conditions.

8.   In 1956 she married playwright Arthur Miller, she stopped working with Greene after
     making *Prince and the Showgirl.*
     A.   In 1956 she married playwright Arthur Miller and she stopped working with Greene
          after making *Prince and the Showgirl.*
     B.   In 1956 she married playwright Arthur Miller, and then she stopped working with
          Greene after making *Prince and the Showgirl.*
     C.   In 1956 she married playwright Arthur Miller she stopped working with Greene after
          making *Prince and the Showgirl.*

9.   She was divorced from Miller in 1961 and she was hospitalized for a mental breakdown.
     A.   She was divorced from Miller in 1961, and she was hospitalized for a mental
          breakdown.
     B.   She was divorced from Miller in 1961, she was hospitalized for a mental breakdown.
     C.   She was divorced from Miller in 1961 and, she was hospitalized for a mental
          breakdown.

10. She never finished *Something's Got to Give* on August 5, 1962 she was found dead.
     A.   She never finished *Something's Got to Give,* on August 5, 1962 she was found dead.
     B.   Never finishing *Something's Got to Give,* Monroe was found dead on August 5, 1962.
     C.   She never finished *Something's Got to Give,* August 5, 1962 she was found dead.

Making Sentence Parts Work Together

Diagnostic Test

Each of the following sentences contains a blank. Choose the answer (A, B, or C) that best completes the sentence.

1. You should _____.
    A. take your prescription to the pharmacy, having it filled, and take some immediately
    B. take your prescription to the pharmacy, have it filled, and taking some immediately
    C. take your prescription to the pharmacy, have it filled, and take some immediately

2. The smell of the cleaning solution was overwhelming; Patricia began coughing, her eyes began watering, and _____.
    A. she wheezed
    B. she began wheezing
    C. she began to wheeze

3. Joe and his friends were in the living room, on the porch, and _____.
    A. the yard
    B. they were around the yard
    C. around the yard

4. Donovan and _____ ate soup together at the restaurant.
    A. myself
    B. me
    C. I

5. That argument is between _____.
    A. him and me
    B. him and myself
    C. he and I

6. At the local bowling alley, Cathy, _____ has a 160 bowling average, was the high scorer of the week with a 275.
    A. who
    B. whom
    C. whose

7. Josh is a better soccer player than _____.
    A. himself
    B. he
    C. him

For questions 8–10, pick the sentence (A, B, or C) that is most clear in meaning.

8. A. George informed Jay of his company's problems.
    B. George said to Jay, "My company has problems."
    C. Jay informed George of his company's problems.

9.   A.   Kelli is the most good cheerleader I have ever seen.
      B.   Kelli is the more better cheerleader I have ever seen.
      C.   Kelli is the best cheerleader I have ever seen.

10.   A.   After the plumber was done, Sean carefully checked the work done in the bathroom.
      B.   Carefully after the plumber was done, Sean checked the work done in the bathroom.
      C.   After the plumber was done, Sean checked the work carefully done in the bathroom.

Practicing More with Verbs

Diagnostic Test

Each of the following sentences contains a blank. Choose the answer (A, B, or C) that will complete the sentence correctly.

1. The man _____ through the alley.
    A. creeped
    B. creep
    C. crept

2. The teachers _____ the classes as a team.
    A. teaches
    B. taught
    C. has taught

3. Daphne _____ the true meaning of the poem.
    A. sought
    B. has seeked
    C. seek

4. Stewart's boat has not _____ since he got it patched.
    A. sink
    B. sank
    C. sunk

5. The dog must have _____ I was opening the can.
    A. knew
    B. known
    C. knowed

6. Even though Miriam wanted the red dress, _____
    A. she settles for the blue one.
    B. she settle for the blue one.
    C. she settled for the blue one.

7. Tag and hopscotch were two of my favorite games as a child; _____
    A. the games keep me in shape then.
    B. the games kept me in shape then.
    C. the games has kept me in shape then.

8. Scott gave his wife a huge bouquet for their anniversary, and _____
    A. she took it with her to work.
    B. she take it with her to work.
    C. she has took it with her to work.

9.   If the television show goes off the air, _____
     A.   then Derrick will be sad.
     B.   then Derrick is sad.
     C.   then Derrick was sad.

10. The convention attracted some very strange people _____
     A.   who dresses in costume.
     B.   who were dressed in costume.
     C.   who was dressed in costume.

Exercise A

Choose the answer (A, B, or C) in which the underlined irregular verb is used correctly.

1. A. With January's storm, the iced branches of the birch had <u>bent</u> nearly to the ground.
    B. With January's storm, the iced branches of the birch had <u>bended</u> nearly to the ground.
    C. With January's storm, the iced branches of the birch had <u>bend</u> nearly to the ground.

2. A. Moments after the clock struck midnight, the boy <u>creep</u> downstairs as quietly as he could.
    B. Moments after the clock struck midnight, the boy <u>creeped</u> downstairs as quietly as he could.
    C. Moments after the clock struck midnight, the boy <u>crept</u> downstairs as quietly as he could.

3. A. In no time at all he <u>won</u> them over with his sweetness.
    B. In no time at all he <u>winned</u> them over with his sweetness.
    C. In no time at all he <u>win</u> them over with his sweetness.

4. A. He <u>wrung</u> out the sweater despite the instructions on the label.
    B. He <u>wring</u> out the sweater despite the instructions on the label.
    C. He <u>rung</u> out the sweater despite the instructions on the label.

5. A. The counselor asked them, "How much warm clothing have you <u>brung</u>?"
    B. The counselor asked them, "How much warm clothing have you <u>bring</u>?"
    C. The counselor asked them, "How much warm clothing have you <u>brought</u>?"

6. A. Singing softly to herself, the girl <u>dug</u> all afternoon in the warm white sand.
    B. Singing softly to herself, the girl <u>digged</u> all afternoon in the warm white sand.
    C. Singing softly to herself, the girl <u>dig</u> all afternoon in the warm white sand.

7. A. He <u>feel</u> a keen sense of hunger all afternoon that interfered with his concentration.
    B. He <u>felt</u> a keen sense of hunger all afternoon that interfered with his concentration.
    C. He <u>feeled</u> a keen sense of hunger all afternoon that interfered with his concentration.

8. A. I have <u>bet</u> him that the team will make the finals this year.
    B. I have <u>beat</u> him that the team will make the finals this year.
    C. I have <u>betted</u> him that the team will make the finals this year.

9. A. She really hopes her grandmother's beautifully ornate wedding dress will <u>fit</u> her.
    B. She really hopes her grandmother's beautifully ornate wedding dress will <u>fitted</u> her.
    C. She really hopes her grandmother's beautifully ornate wedding dress will <u>fat</u> her.

10. A. The date has been <u>setted</u>; he will begin his cross-country trip on June 18.
    B. The date has been <u>sat</u>; he will begin his cross-country trip on June 18.
    C. The date has been <u>set</u>; he will begin his cross-country trip on June 18.

11. A. Jane has <u>becomed</u> quite excited about the pediatric residency in nephrology.
    B. Jane has <u>became</u> quite excited about the pediatric residency in nephrology.
    C. Jane has <u>become</u> quite excited about the pediatric residency in nephrology.

12. A. He went last month to the concert in Pigeon Forge; his brother Al <u>goed</u> with him.
    B. He went last month to the concert in Pigeon Forge; his brother Al <u>gone</u> with him.
    C. He went last month to the concert in Pigeon Forge; his brother Al <u>went</u> with him.

13. A. She went to the anti-vivisection demonstration, even though her mother strictly <u>forbade</u> her.
    B. She went to the anti-vivisection demonstration, even though her mother strictly <u>forbid</u> her.
    C. She went to the anti-vivisection demonstration, even though her mother strictly <u>forbidden</u> her.

14. A. Has she <u>get</u> all her letters of recommendation for her graduate school application?
    B. Has she <u>got</u> all her letters of recommendation for her graduate school application?
    C. Has she <u>gotten</u> all her letters of recommendation for her graduate school application?

15. A. They walked all the way, and an icy February wind <u>blowed</u> from the north.
    B. They walked all the way, and an icy February wind <u>blew</u> from the north.
    C. They walked all the way, and an icy February wind <u>blown</u> from the north.

Exercise B

Choose the answer (A, B, or C) in which the underlined irregular verb is used correctly.

1. A. When the child smiled up at me, I knew he had <u>broken</u> the plate.
    B. When the child smiled up at me, I knew he had <u>broke</u> the plate.
    C. When the child smiled up at me, I knew he had <u>break</u> the plate.

2. A. For dinner she has <u>chosen</u> a Mandarin chicken dish with rice and vegetables.
    B. For dinner she has <u>chose</u> a Mandarin chicken dish with rice and vegetables.
    C. For dinner she has <u>choose</u> a Mandarin chicken dish with rice and vegetables.

3. A. As he told the story, his mother <u>began</u> to bubble with laughter.
    B. As he told the story, his mother <u>begun</u> to bubble with laughter.
    C. As he told the story, his mother <u>begin</u> to bubble with laughter.

4. A. The player <u>throw</u> the ball to second after he caught the fly ball.
    B. The player <u>threw</u> the ball to second after he caught the fly ball.
    C. The player <u>thrown</u> the ball to second after he caught the fly ball.

5. A. After the child had <u>drank</u> all his milk, he began to doze off in her arms.
    B. After the child had <u>drink</u> all his milk, he began to doze off in her arms.
    C. After the child had <u>drunk</u> all his milk, he began to doze off in her arms.

6. A. After a scrumptious dinner, it was revealed that he had <u>stole</u> the recipe from the innkeeper's desk when we stayed last year.
    B. After a scrumptious dinner, it was revealed that he had <u>stolen</u> the recipe from the innkeeper's desk when we stayed last year.
    C. After a scrumptious dinner, it was revealed that he had <u>stealed</u> the recipe from the innkeeper's desk when we stayed last year.

7. A. Has young Harold <u>put</u> on his winter coat, scarf, and gloves?
    B. Has young Harold <u>putted</u> on his winter coat, scarf, and gloves?
    C. Has young Harold <u>pet</u> on his winter coat, scarf, and gloves?

8. A. The baseball card, if it was in good condition, must have <u>cost</u> a great deal.
    B. The baseball card, if it was in good condition, must have <u>cast</u> a great deal.
    C. The baseball card, if it was in good condition, must have <u>costed</u> a great deal.

9. A. Before she left, she <u>mean</u> to set the VCR to record the Civil War documentary.
    B. Before she left, she <u>mint</u> to set the VCR to record the Civil War documentary.
    C. Before she left, she <u>meant</u> to set the VCR to record the Civil War documentary.

10. A. The agitated visitor tossed, turned, and hardly <u>sleeped</u> a wink.
    B. The agitated visitor tossed, turned, and hardly <u>sleep</u> a wink.
    C. The agitated visitor tossed, turned, and hardly <u>slept</u> a wink.

11. A. Deep in the woods is the fort the brothers had <u>build</u> as children.
    B. Deep in the woods is the fort the brothers had <u>built</u> as children.
    C. Deep in the woods is the fort the brothers had <u>builded</u> as children.

12. A. I've <u>spoken</u> to him about the class trip; I will chaperone this year.
    B. I've <u>spoke</u> to him about the class trip; I will chaperone this year.
    C. I've <u>speak</u> to him about the class trip; I will chaperone this year.

13. A. Last September he had <u>taken</u> her back to Provence, where she was born.
    B. Last September he had <u>taked</u> her back to Provence, where she was born.
    C. Last September he had <u>took</u> her back to Provence, where she was born.

14. A. The gentlemen <u>strode</u> through the office in their elegant suits before the awards dinner.
    B. The gentlemen <u>stride</u> through the office in their elegant suits before the awards dinner.
    C. The gentlemen <u>stridden</u> through the office in their elegant suits before the awards dinner.

15. A. That young journalist has <u>written</u> an especially sensitive account of the tragedy.
    B. That young journalist has <u>write</u> an especially sensitive account of the tragedy.
    C. That young journalist has <u>wrote</u> an especially sensitive account of the tragedy.

Exercise C

Identify if the sentence is active (A) or passive (P). If the original sentence is active, rewrite the sentence in passive voice. If the original sentence is passive, rewrite the sentence in active voice.

_____ 1. The buffet was enjoyed by the party guests.

_____

_____ 2. Sally took notes at the meeting.

_____

_____ 3. In the train station, the people waited for the train.

_____

_____ 4. Will, the assistant manager, was helped by the other workers.

_____

_____ 5. Delicious iced tea was made by Marva.

_____

_____ 6. The branches were blown by the wind.

_____

_____ 7. Gene gave a pair of earrings to his wife, Gina.

_____

_____ 8. The teacher gave the class homework.

_____

_____ 9. Tim, emerging from his car, waved to Maria and Sonya.

_____

_____ 10. A grand entrance was made by the movie star.

_____

_____ 11. The computers were rebooted by Linda.

_____

_____ 12. Last fall, football was watched by a record number of people.

_____

_____ 13. The trash cans in front of Bob's house were run over by a teenage driver.

_____

_____ 14. During the car accident, the seatbelt protected Julie.

_____

_____ 15. On Thursday, the nurses gave at least one hundred flu shots.

_____

Exercise D

Some of the verbs in the following passage are incorrect. Find the errors and correct them.

That gloomy night, an angry wind blown so hard that the branches of the large oak tree tapped continually at his window. Soon, the small child was so frightened by the storm that he creeped into his parents' room. As always, his parents had been sleeping soundly and hear nothing. As he set quietly on the floor, by his mother's side of the bed, he though he sees a large arm come out thru his parents' window. At once he start shivering. He then crawl into bed next to his mother, had closed his eyes tight to shut it all out, and awakes finally to the morning sun that shined brilliantly in the same sky that appeared so ominous the night before.

Exercise E

Some of the verbs in the following paragraphs are incorrect. Find the errors and correct them.

Ian Fleming's James Bond has became the most successful set of movie sequels, with twenty films total. Fleming begins to write the books in 1952. In 1962, Harry Saltzman and Albert Cubby Broccoli begun filming the books, beginning with *Dr. No.* Sean Connery was chose as the first James Bond. In these movies, Bond always enjoyed the company of beautiful women. There was also gadgets and fancy cars for Bond, too. Sean Connery done five movies before Roger Moore takes over as James Bond. Moore made seven movies as James Bond. He could of made more, but he decided to retire. Timothy Dalton, David Niven, and George Lazenby have each took a shot at Bond fame. The most recent Bond is Pierce Brosnan who has been in four Bond movies. Ian Fleming would of been proud of his secret agent.

Exercise F

Find the verb errors in the following sentences and correct them.

1. Quickly closes the door!

   _____

   _____

2. Do your mother have papers and projects from when you are in elementary school?

   _____

   _____

3. Websites that are about urban legends explains how each legend got started.

   _____

   _____

4. Everyone in the classes have written a paper for the contest.

   _____

   _____

5. When the alarm sound, you should leaves the building and meet in the designated place.

   _____

   _____

6. The young boys fighted on the playground.

   _____

   _____

7. Has you heared that the new Harry Potter movie will soon be out?

   _____

   _____

8. What done Sharon have for breakfast?

   _____

   _____

9.   Nestled in their beds, the children slept soundly.

_____

_____

10.   Julian was mistook for a criminal because he had the same kind of car.

_____

_____

Mastery Test

Each of the following sentences contain two blanks. Choose the answer (A, B, or C) that will complete the sentence correctly.

1. Barry and Jason _____ the phone number, but they _____ it.
   A. knows, loses
   B. knew, lost
   C. knew, lose

2. The magazines Maria _____ included *Newsweek* and *Time;* she _____ *TV Guide* every week, too.
   A. reads, buys
   B. reads, bought
   C. read, bought

3. When Tabitha _____ up, she _____ her warm bed to get ready for work.
   A. woke, left
   B. wakes, left
   C. woken, leaves

4. Prior to the flight today, Samantha _____ to London because she _____ to see Big Ben.
   A. flies, wants
   B. flew, wants
   C. had flown, wanted

5. Gabrielle _____ the yellow dress, and her mother _____ when she saw Gabrielle in it.
   A. choosed, weeps
   B. chose, wept
   C. has choosen, had weeped

In questions 6–10, choose the answer (A, B, or C) that uses the correct sequence of tenses.

6. A. We hoped that we will seen her soon.
   B. We hopes that we sees her soon.
   C. We hoped that we would see her soon.

7. A. *Death of a Salesman* is one of Arthur Miller's most famous plays; he has written it in 1949.
   B. *Death of a Salesman* is one of Arthur Miller's most famous plays; he wrote it in 1949.
   C. *Death of a Salesman* was one of Arthur Miller's most famous plays; he had written it in 1949.

8. A. If Daisy had wanted to be here before Joe left, she would have been here by now.
   B. If Daisy wants to be here before Joe left, she would have been here by now.
   C. If Daisy wanted to be here before Joe left, she would of been here by now.

9. A. Lamar should have bought his television from our local store; then he have a warranty.
   B. Lamar should of bought his television from our local store; then he would have a warranty.
   C. Lamar should have bought his television from the local store; then he would have had a warranty.

10. A. If Maxine were a lawyer, not a paralegal, I would have her help me.
    B. If Maxine was a lawyer, not a paralegal, I would have her help me.
    C. If Maxine was a lawyer, not a paralegal, I would had her help me.

Using Correct Capitalization and Punctuation

Diagnostic Test

In questions 1–5, choose the answer (A, B, or C) that shows all the commas used correctly.

1. A. The DVD player the VCR, and the stereo receiver are all wired together.
    B. The DVD player the VCR and the stereo receiver, are all wired together.
    C. The DVD player, the VCR, and the stereo receiver are all wired together.

2. A. On Saturday, Sara went to Disney World with Melanie and Kristy.
    B. On Saturday Sara went to Disney World with Melanie, and Kristy.
    C. On Saturday Sara went to Disney World, with Melanie and Kristy.

3. A. Michael and Michelle Watkins were married on February 14, 2004, in Seattle.
    B. Michael and Michelle Watkins were married on February 14, 2004 in Seattle.
    C. Michael, and Michelle Watkins were married on February 14, 2004 in Seattle.

4. A. Lori wants to get a new car so, she has been doing research on the Internet.
    B. Lori wants to get a new car, so she has been doing research on the Internet.
    C. Lori wants to get a new car so she has been doing research on the Internet.

5. A. Daria, who loves Irish setters, is getting a puppy for her birthday.
    B. Daria, who loves Irish setters, is getting a puppy, for her birthday.
    C. Daria who loves Irish setters, is getting a puppy for her birthday.

In questions 6–10, read the two sentences and choose whether A or B shows the words capitalized correctly.

6. A. The national conference on aging is on the college campus.
    B. The National Conference on Aging is on the college campus.

7. A. The Policeman said, "can I see your driver's license and registration?"
    B. The policeman said, "Can I see your driver's license and registration?"

8. A. When Amy goes to Santa Monica in September, she will need a light jacket.
    B. When Amy goes to Santa Monica in september, she will need a light jacket.

9. A. Ted's main Office is near Downtown Detroit.
    B. Ted's main office is near downtown Detroit.

10. A. The new Mall will open in Spring 2006.
    B. The new mall will open in spring 2006.

Exercise A

Read the two sentences and choose whether A or B shows the words capitalized correctly.

1. A. "To err is human, to forgive, divine," advised Alexander Pope in his well-read Essay *An Essay on Criticism.*
    B. "To err is human, to forgive, divine," advised Alexander Pope in his well-read essay *An Essay on Criticism.*

2. A. I remember reading the essay in an english survey course with professor Engleston last fall at the University.
    B. I remember reading the essay in an English survey course with Professor Engleston last fall at the university.

3. A. One of her favorite rabbis used to remind his young students of Sophocles' wise words, "He who throws away a friend is as bad as he who throws away life."
    B. One of her favorite Rabbis used to remind his young students of Sophocles' wise words, "He who throws away a friend is as bad as he who throws away life."

4. A. "Be slow in choosing a friend, slower in changing," rabbi Fein was also fond of saying, quoting Benjamin Franklin.
    B. "Be slow in choosing a friend, slower in changing," Rabbi Fein was also fond of saying, quoting Benjamin Franklin.

5. A. She hails from the midwest where she was born in Morning Sun, Iowa; today she teaches french at a private college in the northeast.
    B. She hails from the Midwest where she was born in Morning Sun, Iowa; today she teaches French at a private college in the Northeast.

6. A. Occasionally, during the Spring semester, she teaches a course on French poets for the English department.
    B. Occasionally, during the spring semester, she teaches a course on French poets for the English Department.

7. A. He spoke with great pride when he said, "My son is in the Boy Scouts."
    B. He spoke with great pride when he said, "my son is in the boy scouts."

8. A. "They had a fundraiser for the March of dimes," he boasted, "And collected over two thousand dollars."
    B. "They had a fundraiser for the March of Dimes," he boasted, "and collected over two thousand dollars."

9. A. My Grandmother often said, "Thanksgiving is my favorite holiday."
    B. My grandmother often said, "Thanksgiving is my favorite holiday."

10. A. "It reminds me," Grandma would say, "of all the many blessings I have."
    B. "It reminds me," grandma would say, "Of all the many blessings I have."

11. A. His Father, judge Minter, read every book he could find at the Haddonfield Library on the bill of rights
    B. His father, Judge Minter, read every book he could find at the Haddonfield Library on the Bill of Rights.

12. A. Mrs. Minter is fond of Victorian Novelist George Eliot; she is reading her novel *Middlemarch* and says she will finish by november 9.

     B. Mrs. Minter is fond of Victorian novelist George Eliot; she is reading her novel *Middlemarch* and says she will finish by November 9.

13. A. While his family was camping at Lake Hopatcong last summer, Bill finished his doctoral dissertation at the Free Public Library.

     B. While his family was camping at lake Hopatcong last Summer, Bill finished his doctoral dissertation at the Free Public Library.

14. A. "Nothing I can remember," said Evelyn, "is as vivid as the first Winter I learned to skate on the Lake."

     B. "Nothing I can remember," said Evelyn, "is as vivid as the first winter I learned to skate on the lake."

15. A. He has lived on Marner Avenue ever since he began working as a clerk at the Boyleston Post Office.

     B. He has lived on Marner avenue ever since he began working as a Clerk at the Boyleston post office.

Exercise B

Read the two sentences and choose whether A or B shows the words capitalized correctly.

1. A. Jacquelyn Kennedy has been regarded as the most elegant First Lady, according to the article in Sunday's *New York Times*.
    B. Jacquelyn Kennedy has been regarded as the most elegant first lady, according to the article in sunday's *New York Times*.

2. A. The Clerk in the Cereal Aisle commented that nabisco Shredded Wheat was her favorite shredded wheat cereal.
    B. The clerk in the cereal aisle commented that Nabisco Shredded Wheat was her favorite shredded wheat cereal.

3. A. "It has no added sugar," she said, "Nor any added salt."
    B. "It has no added sugar," she said, "nor any added salt."

4. A. Some wisecracker behind me added, "nor any taste!"
    B. Some wisecracker behind me added, "Nor any taste!"

5. A. Mr. Etting plans to drive west across the country to visit Grandpa in Northern California.
    B. Mr. Etting plans to drive West across the country to visit Grandpa in northern California.

6. A. They were in the U.S. Marine Corps together and haven't seen each other since the Spring of 1968.
    B. They were in the U.S. Marine Corps together and haven't seen each other since the spring of 1968.

7. A. Janet's High School reunion is next Saturday night; she attended Brower High School in the late 1970s.
    B. Janet's high school reunion is next Saturday night; she attended Brower High School in the late 1970s.

8. A. She asked her sister, "Are Mary and Joe both going to see the movie at Loew's Theater?"
    B. She asked her Sister, "are Mary and Joe both going to see the movie at Loew's theater?"

9. A. I ran into an old friend, Amy, at the post office on New Year's Eve.
    B. I ran into an old friend, Amy, at the Post Office on New Year's eve.

10. A. Ted has an appointment with a pediatric ophthalmologist named Dr. Wesler.
    B. Ted has an appointment with a Pediatric Ophthalmologist named Dr. Wesler.

11. A. "I went to see the Doctor last February around Presidents' Day."
    B. "I went to see the doctor last February around Presidents' Day."

12. A. She agreed, "Chapel Hill, North Carolina, is a beautiful college town."
    B. She agreed, "chapel Hill, North Carolina, is a beautiful College town."

13. A. John's class is visiting the Franklin Institute, which has always been one of my favorite science museums.
     B. John's class is visiting the Franklin Institute, which has always been one of my favorite Science Museums.

14. A. He said to me when he called, "We had a great time yesterday at the basketball game."
     B. He said to me when he called, "we had a great time yesterday at the Basketball game."

15. A. "Yes," I agreed with him, "it was wonderful to relive those memories from the old university days."
     B. "Yes," I agreed with him, "It was wonderful to relive those memories from the old University days."

Exercise C

Read the two sentences and choose whether A or B shows the words capitalized correctly.

1. A. Mr. greene teaches American History.
    B. Mr. Greene teaches American history.

2. A. Lake Superior is one of the Great Lakes.
    B. Lake superior is one of the great lakes.

3. A. The new CD is titled *Run in the Race.*
    B. The new CD is titled *run in the Race.*

4. A. Jackie's favorite Singers are Brooks and dunn.
    B. Jackie's favorite singers are Brooks and Dunn.

5. A. Diana wants to go on a cruise in the Fall.
    B. Diana wants to go on a cruise in the fall.

6. A. In 1997, I took three French classes to improve myself.
    B. In 1997, I took three french classes to improve myself.

7. A. During the Winter, the local College has a month-long break.
    B. During the winter, the local college has a month-long break.

8. A. Deborah loves shopping with Mother and me.
    B. Deborah loves shopping with mother and me.

9. A. Janice has a class with Professor Hale.
    B. Janice has a Class with professor Hale.

10. A. The Dean of the University has worked there for twenty years.
    B. The dean of the university has worked there for twenty years.

11. A. "My cat loves tuna," said Minnie, "and other fish flavors."
    B. "My cat loves tuna," said Minnie, "And other fish flavors."

12. A. Sandra's favorite television show is on Tuesday nights.
    B. Sandra's favorite Television show is on tuesday nights.

13. A. Jacksonville, Florida, is North of Orlando.
    B. Jacksonville, Florida, is north of Orlando.

14. A. The Mississippi river begins its journey North in Louisiana.
    B. The Mississippi River begins its journey north in Louisiana.

15. A. The new Ford F-150 is a great truck.
    B. The new ford F-150 is a great truck.

Exercise D

Read the two sentences and choose whether A or B shows the words capitalized correctly.

1. A. Dr. Martin Luther King, Jr., has a National Holiday named for him.
    B. Dr. Martin Luther King, Jr., has a national holiday named for him.

2. A. In December, Pam visited her Grandmother.
    B. In December, Pam visited her grandmother.

3. A. Nick would like to move to the Midwest.
    B. Nick would like to move to the midwest.

4. A. Debbie wants a Chevy truck.
    B. Debbie wants a chevy truck.

5. A. Beginning in july, Charles began to work out at the Gym.
    B. Beginning in July, Charles began to work out at the gym.

6. A. The Governor will speak at the University.
    B. The governor will speak at the university.

7. A. She sings in a cabaret; she wants to record an album.
    B. She sings in a Cabaret; she wants to record an Album.

8. A. "I want to sleep," said Russell, "But it's still daylight."
    B. "I want to sleep," said Russell, "but it's still daylight."

9. A. Ian took a trip to the Museum with the Greek exhibit.
    B. Ian took a trip to the museum with the Greek exhibit.

10. A. The Smithsonian Museum in Washington, D.C., has a large collection of television memorabilia.
    B. The Smithsonian museum in Washington, D.C., has a large collection of Television memorabilia.

11. A. Normally shy, Quentin got excited about his Math class.
    B. Normally shy, Quentin got excited about his math class.

12. A. There will be a special furniture sale on Tuesday.
    B. There will be a special Furniture Sale on Tuesday.

13. A. My club always has a Pumpkin sale fundraiser in october.
    B. My club always has a pumpkin sale fundraiser in October.

14. A. Todd's Boy Scout troop always camps in a national forest.
    B. Todd's Boy Scout troop always camps in a National Forest.

15. A. Brenda said, "He is my husband."
    B. Brenda said, "he is my husband."

Exercise E

In each of the following groups of sentences, choose the letter (A, B, or C) that shows a sentence that uses commas correctly.

1. A. "I do believe," said the enthusiastic professor, "you will appreciate our next novel by William Faulkner."
    B. "I do believe" said the enthusiastic professor, "you will appreciate, our next novel by William Faulkner."
    C. "I do believe," said the enthusiastic professor "you will appreciate our next novel by William Faulkner."

2. A. "*The Sound and the Fury,* is one of Faulkner's best known works," she told the class, "published in 1929."
    B. "*The Sound and the Fury* is one of Faulkner's best known works," she told the class, "published in 1929."
    C. "*The Sound and the Fury* is one of Faulkner's best known works," she told the class "published in 1929."

3. A. "In this novel we see the Compsons again," she told the students "in all their dysfunction."
    B. "In this novel, we see the Compsons again," she told the students, "in all their dysfunction."
    C. "In this novel, we see the Compsons again" she told the students, "in all their dysfunction."

4. A. "Through much of Faulkner the author examines the sorrows of fathers and sons, and, he reveals the disadvantage and restlessness of mothers and daughters."
    B. "Through much of Faulkner, the author examines the sorrows of fathers and sons, and he reveals the disadvantage, and restlessness, of mothers and daughters."
    C. "Through much of Faulkner, the author examines the sorrows of fathers and sons, and he reveals the disadvantage and restlessness of mothers and daughters."

5. A. Female students in the class who greatly outnumbered the males, commented on the author's characterization of Caddy Compson.
    B. Female students in the class, who greatly outnumbered the males, commented, on the author's characterization of Caddy Compson.
    C. Female students in the class, who greatly outnumbered the males, commented on the author's characterization of Caddy Compson.

6. A. "It seems," said Janet sitting in the third row, "that Caddy was really the most resourceful, and energetic of all the Compson children."
    B. "It seems" said Janet, sitting in the third row, "that Caddy was really the most resourceful, and energetic of all the Compson children."
    C. "It seems," said Janet, sitting in the third row, "that Caddy was really the most resourceful and energetic of all the Compson children."

7. A. Then Jim remarked, "Yet, it was Quentin, who was given the chance, to go to Harvard."
    B. Then, Jim remarked, "Yet, it was Quentin, who, was given the chance to go to Harvard."
    C. Then, Jim remarked, "Yet, it was Quentin who was given the chance to go to Harvard."

8. A. "I believe, you've both hit on an important issue, for many of Faulkner's readers," said Professor Neidler.
   B. "I believe you've both hit on an important issue for many of Faulkner's readers," said Professor Neidler.
   C. "I believe you've both hit on an important issue, for many of Faulkner's readers" said Professor Neidler.

9. A. "Education doesn't seem to be a choice for Faulkner's female characters," she continued, "No wonder females like Caddy, become dissatisfied, searching for outlets as she did."
   B. "Education doesn't seem to be a choice for Faulkner's female characters," she continued. "No wonder females, like Caddy become dissatisfied, searching for outlets, as she, did."
   C. "Education doesn't seem to be a choice for Faulkner's female characters," she continued. "No wonder females like Caddy become dissatisfied, searching for outlets as she did."

10. A. "Instead, female characters like Dilsey who exemplify selfless devotion to others, are the females who endure, and this theme has opened the door for feminist critics."
    B. "Instead, female characters like Dilsey, who exemplify selfless devotion to others, are the females who endure, and this theme has opened the door for feminist critics."
    C. "Instead, female characters like Dilsey, who exemplify selfless devotion to others, are the females who endure and this theme has opened the door for feminist critics."

Exercise F

In each of the following groups of sentences, choose the letter (A, B, or C) that shows the commas used correctly.

1. A. F. Scott Fitzgerald, whose most widely read novel, is *The Great Gatsby,* is often studied along with the works of Ernest Hemingway, Gertrude Stein, and other American authors of the 1920s and 1930s.
    B. F. Scott Fitzgerald, whose most widely read novel is *The Great Gatsby,* is often studied along with the works of Ernest Hemingway, Gertrude Stein, and other American authors of the 1920s and 1930s.
    C. F. Scott Fitzgerald whose most widely read novel is *The Great Gatsby,* is often studied along with the works of Ernest Hemingway, Gertrude Stein, and other American authors of the 1920s and 1930s.

2. A. From Fitzgerald's main character, Jay Gatsby, readers see love that is destructive, love that undoes the man with its tenderness.
    B. From Fitzgerald's main character, Jay Gatsby, readers see, love that is destructive, love that undoes the man with its tenderness.
    C. From Fitzgerald's main character, Jay Gatsby, readers, see love that is destructive, love that undoes the man with its tenderness.

3. A. *The Great Gatsby* like very few other American novels retains its importance, even after three quarters of a century.
    B. *The Great Gatsby* like very few other American novels, retains its importance, even after three quarters of a century.
    C. *The Great Gatsby,* like very few other American novels, retains its importance, even after three quarters of a century.

4. A. Even though some readers have charged, Gatsby's character as being less than credible, the incredible significance he implies seems timeless.
    B. Even though some readers have charged Gatsby's character as being less than credible, the incredible significance he implies seems timeless.
    C. Even though some readers have charged Gatsby's character as being less than credible the incredible significance he implies seems timeless.

5. A. Gatsby can be said to symbolize America itself, with America building itself upon a dream, the "American Dream."
    B. Gatsby, can be said to symbolize America itself, with America building itself, upon a dream, the "American Dream."
    C. Gatsby can be said to symbolize America itself, with America building itself upon a dream the "American Dream."

6. A. Although the novel can be read as an exploration of the American Dream in the face of great adversity, at its depths is the theme of reality and its relation to illusion.
    B. Although the novel can be read as an exploration of the American Dream in the face of great adversity at its depths is the theme of reality and its relation to illusion.
    C. Although, the novel can be read as an exploration of the American Dream in the face of great adversity, at its depths is the theme of reality and its relation to illusion.

7. A. The author however, seems to suggest that the reality is embodied in Gatsby, that reality is a spiritual thing.
    B. The author however seems to suggest, that the reality is embodied in Gatsby, that reality is a spiritual thing.
    C. The author, however, seems to suggest that the reality is embodied in Gatsby, that reality is a spiritual thing.

8. A. The author implies that, for Gatsby reality becomes what one believes, and, that belief becomes who one is.
    B. The author, implies that, for Gatsby, reality becomes what one believes, and that belief, becomes who one is.
    C. The author implies that, for Gatsby, reality becomes what one believes, and that belief becomes who one is.

9. A. Gatsby, became the man who stood at the door of his mansion, wishing his guests a good night; for the reader, this is a reality.
    B. Gatsby became the man who stood at the door of his mansion, wishing his guests a good night; for the reader, this is a reality.
    C. Gatsby became the man, who stood at the door of his mansion, wishing his guests a good night; for the reader, this, is a reality.

10. A. Gatsby's union with Daisy, in spite of her marriage to Tom, is the only reality he knows, for her responsibility to her marriage is hers, and not even his concern.
    B. Gatsby's union with Daisy in spite of her marriage to Tom, is the only reality he knows, for her responsibility to her marriage is hers, and not even his concern.
    C. Gatsby's union with Daisy in spite of her marriage to Tom, is the only reality he knows, for her responsibility to her marriage is hers and not even his concern.

11. A. The novel's illusion for so many readers, is embodied in the characterization of Daisy, in her own hollow debutante life of meaninglessness.
    B. The novel's illusion, for, so many readers, is embodied in the characterization of Daisy, in her own hollow debutante life of meaninglessness.
    C. The novel's illusion, for so many readers, is embodied in the characterization of Daisy, in her own hollow debutante life of meaninglessness.

12. A. The author illustrates this hollowness of Daisy, this inability she has for understanding consequence, in her indifference toward the death she caused.
    B. The author illustrates this hollowness of Daisy, this inability she has for understanding consequence in her indifference toward the death, she caused.
    C. The author illustrates this hollowness of Daisy, this inability, she has for understanding consequence, in her indifference toward the death she caused.

13. A. These same readers notice how, for Gatsby, Daisy does not exist in reality in herself but, rather as a green light beckoning Gatsby into his vision.
    B. These same readers notice how, for Gatsby, Daisy does not exist in reality in herself, but rather as a green light beckoning Gatsby into his vision.
    C. These same readers notice, how, for Gatsby, Daisy does not exist in reality in herself, but, rather as a green light beckoning Gatsby into his vision.

14. A. Tragically, Gatsby's failure to discriminate between reality and illusion brings about his death, an incident fleshly concrete in reality.
   B. Tragically, Gatsby's failure to discriminate between reality and illusion, brings about his death, an incident fleshly concrete in reality.
   C. Tragically, Gatsby's failure, to discriminate between reality and illusion brings about his death, an incident fleshly concrete in reality.

15. A. In the end, however, Gatsby, in all his blindness and ignorance of reality-based America, is the character for whom the reader holds hope.
   B. In the end, however, Gatsby in all his blindness and ignorance of reality-based America, is the character for whom the reader holds hope.
   C. In the end, however, Gatsby in all his blindness and ignorance of reality-based America is the character for whom the reader holds hope.

Exercise G

Choose the letter (A, B, or C) in which all the punctuation is used correctly.

1. A. Haven't you wondered whether theres a football team?
    B. Haven't you wondered whether there's a football team?
    C. Havent you wondered whether theres a football team?

2. A. The bad attitude of other people makes me unhappy, I like to stay happy.
    B. The bad attitude of other people makes me unhappy I like to stay happy.
    C. The bad attitude of other people makes me unhappy, and I like to stay happy.

3. A. Since I had always wanted to see Alaska, I went there last summer.
    B. Since I had always wanted to see Alaska I went there last summer.
    C. Since, I had always wanted to see Alaska, I went there last summer.

4. A. "I wanted to believe her," he said "but I just couldn't."
    B. "I wanted to believe her" he said "but I just couldnt."
    C. "I wanted to believe her," he said, "but I just couldn't."

5. A. Nora bought bread and milk; in addition, she bought cat food.
    B. Nora bought bread and milk, in addition, she bought cat food.
    C. Nora bought bread and milk in addition she bought cat food.

6. A. Listening to her stereo and reading love stories are my sisters chief pleasures.
    B. Listening to her stereo and reading love stories are my sister's chief pleasures.
    C. Listening to her stereo, and reading love stories are my sister's chief pleasures.

7. A. Margie has invited our class to her parents mansion for our reunion.
    B. Margie has invited our class to her parents' mansion for our reunion.
    C. Margie has invited our class to her parents mansion, for our reunion.

8. A. Because Hector almost failed the test, he got a tutor to help him.
    B. Because, Hector almost failed the test, he got a tutor to help him.
    C. Because Hector almost failed the test he got a tutor to help him.

9. A. She closed the door yet she didn't keep her voice down.
    B. She closed the door, yet she didnt keep her voice down.
    C. She closed the door, yet she didn't keep her voice down.

10. A. He told, I believe, a lie.
    B. He told I believe, a lie.
    C. He told I believe a lie.

11. A. Victor loves to eat potato chips in his ice cream, indeed, he loves the combination of salt and sweet.
    B. Victor loves to eat potato chips in his ice cream indeed he loves the combination of salt and sweet.
    C. Victor loves to eat potato chips in his ice cream; indeed, he loves the combination of salt and sweet.

12. A. "If you will go out with me," said Bill "I will take you to a very expensive restaurant."
    B. "If you will go out with me," said Bill, "I will take you to a very expensive restaurant."
    C. "If you will go out with me" said Bill "I will take you to a very expensive restaurant."

13. A. Gerardo married at age twenty, moreover, he found himself working a minimum wage job.
    B. Gerardo married at age twenty moreover he found himself working a minimum wage job.
    C. Gerardo married at age twenty; moreover, he found himself working a minimum wage job.

14. A. Whenever Angela played the piano, her mother realized how talented Angela was.
    B. Whenever Angela played the piano her mother realized how talented Angela was.
    C. Whenever, Angela played the piano, her mother realized, how talented Angela was.

15. A. I thought *Harry Potter and the Sorcerer's Stone* was her book.
    B. I thought Harry Potter and the Sorcerer's Stone was her book.
    C. I thought *Harry Potter and the Sorcerers Stone* was her's book.

Exercise H

Read the following paragraph and insert the correct capitalization and punctuation marks wherever they are needed.

The Harlem renaissance is noted for the resurgence of African American art. This art which had already earned respect in europe finally found an open door here at home in the United States. poets writers musicians and intellectuals had found a place for themselves. In the New York of the 1920s harlem became a fertile cultural center that fostered and stimulated all forms of the arts. Musicians such as Duke Ellington Louis Armstrong, and Eubie Blake, just to name a very few, joined their musical expression with the written expression of writers such as Langston Hughes, Dorothy West Zora Neale Hurston, and Countee Cullen. Visual arts and theater depicted the political social, and economic conditions of being black in America. The time period remains one of the most uplifting to African Americans as artists.

Exercise I

Read the following paragraphs and insert the correct capitalization and punctuation marks wherever they are needed. Delete unnecessary capitalization or punctuation.

If I could be anywhere, but here, where would I be. I would head South to Key west, to visit my Aunt and Uncle, whom I havent seen in a while. I would enjoy spending time with them, my uncle is a Professional Fisherman, and my aunt Jessie is the best Fish cook I know. Besides the family I love the whole Jimmy buffett life sitting on the beach, listening to country music. Another reason, I would want to be there, is to go scuba diving. The waters one of the calmest places, at least under water. The best time is at night out in the middle of the Ocean looking at the stars. Thats where I would be, if I could be anywhere but here.

Exercise J

Read the following paragraph and insert the correct capitalization and punctuation marks wherever they are needed.

J.d. Salinger was born Jerome David Salinger in New york city on January, 1, 1919. He attended Valley Forge Military academy, in Pennsylvania and he graduated in 1936. After his draft into the United States army, in 1942 and discharge in 1945 he began publishing his short stories regularly in some of the bigger magazines like the *Saturday Evening Post, Esquire,* and the *New Yorker.* His publishing career became most defined by a long relationship with the *New Yorker,* beginning in the late 1940s. Then in 1951 his novel *The Catcher in the Rye* was published and became the work that Salinger is most well known for today.

Exercise K

Read the following paragraph and insert the correct capitalization and punctuation marks wherever they are needed.

Archimedes, 287–212 BC, was a greek Mathematician and Inventor in the fields of Plane and Solid Geometry, arithmetic, and basic mechanics. He was born in syracuse, sicily but he was educated in Alexandria, Egypt, a center for learning, during that time. While he was in egypt he invented the hydraulic screw for raising water, from lower to higher levels. He also defined the Principles of the lever, and invented the compound pulley. Living mostly in Sicily Archimedes devoted his life to research, and experiments. Hes most famous for Archimedes' Principle which is the law of Hydrostatics. The Principle states: that a body immersed in water loses weight equal to the amount of water it displaces. The story claims that Archimedes was taking a bath, when he noticed the water splashing out of his tub. The catapult was another of Archimede's inventions. He also discovered that several properly placed mirrors could start fires on roman ships that were attacking Sicily. Archimedes was a great Mathematician, he was also a great inventor.

Mastery Test

In questions 1–5, choose the sentence (A, B, or C) that has all the commas used correctly.

1. A. Georgio has a life insurance policy worth 2500,000.
    B. Georgio has a life insurance policy worth 2,500,000.
    C. Georgio has a life insurance policy worth 250,000,0.

2. A. "Turn in your papers" said the instructor "and get out your textbooks."
    B. "Turn in your papers," said the instructor "and get out your textbooks."
    C. "Turn in your papers," said the instructor, "and get out your textbooks."

3. A. Pete taught botany, for he loved growing flowers, and vegetables.
    B. Pete taught botany for he loved growing flowers, and vegetables.
    C. Pete taught botany, for he loved growing flowers and vegetables.

4. A. Madonna, who has written a children's book, was on a book tour.
    B. Madonna who has written a children's book was on a book tour.
    C. Madonna, who has written a children's book was on a book tour.

5. A. The weather in Hawaii is almost always in the 70s with a warm, ocean breeze.
    B. The weather, in Hawaii, is almost always in the 70s with a warm, ocean breeze.
    C. The weather in Hawaii is almost always, in the 70s with a warm ocean breeze.

In questions 6–10, choose whether A, B, or C shows the words capitalized correctly.

6. A. "Jane's cousin will be her maid of honor," said my Grandmother.
    B. "Jane's cousin will be her maid of honor," said my grandmother.
    C. "Jane's cousin will be her Maid of Honor," said my grandmother.

7. A. Kevin has a cold, so he needs a Kleenex.
    B. Kevin has a cold, So he needs a Kleenex.
    C. Kevin has a Cold, so he needs a kleenex.

8. A. In the Fall, Phan wants to go to College in the northwest.
    B. In the fall, Phan wants to go to college in the Northwest.
    C. In the Fall, Phan wants to go to college in the Northwest.

9. A. Meghan took four years of German in High School.
    B. Meghan took four years of german in High School.
    C. Meghan took four years of German in high school.

10. A. Brian has a Sony video camera and a Dell computer.
    B. Brian has a sony video camera and a dell computer.
    C. Brian has a Sony Video camera and a Dell Computer.

Paying Attention to Look-Alikes and Sound-Alikes

Diagnostic Test

Choose whether A or B shows the correct form of the underlined word(s).

1.   A.   The <u>principle</u> <u>past</u> me on the street yesterday.
     B.   The <u>principal</u> <u>passed</u> me on the street yesterday.

2.   A.   We had a four <u>course</u> dinner, including <u>dessert</u>.
     B.   We had a four <u>coarse</u> dinner, including <u>desert</u>.

3.   A.   The journalist <u>sited</u> all his sources <u>accept</u> one.
     B.   The journalist <u>cited</u> all his sources <u>except</u> one.

4.   A.   <u>It's</u> the only food <u>they're</u> willing to eat.
     B.   <u>Its</u> the only food <u>there</u> willing to eat.

5.   A.   <u>Your</u> hand is a unique engineering feat with the ability <u>to</u> perform fifty-eight distinct motions.
     B.   <u>You're</u> hand is a unique engineering feat with the ability <u>too</u> perform fifty-eight distinct motions.

6.   A.   The <u>council</u> offered the student valuable <u>advice</u>.
     B.   The <u>counsel</u> offered the student valuable <u>advise</u>.

7.   A.   Now <u>their</u> looking <u>foreword</u> to the next season.
     B.   Now <u>they're</u> looking <u>forward</u> to the next season.

8.   A.   When I was finished, I was <u>too</u> exhausted to do much more <u>than</u> drag myself home.
     B.   When I was finished, I was <u>two</u> exhausted to do much more <u>then</u> drag myself home.

9.   A.   Please, don't <u>breath</u> a word of this to the <u>personal</u> committee.
     B.   Please, don't <u>breathe</u> a word of this to the <u>personnel</u> committee.

10. A.   The <u>whether</u> often <u>effects</u> my mood.
     B.   The <u>weather</u> often <u>affects</u> my mood.

Exercise A

Choose the answer (A, B, or C) that correctly fills the blank.

1. Mary told her to _____ on the bed for an hour before coming down for dinner.
   A. lay
   B. lie
   C. laid

2. She pulled down the shades to darken the room, and then she drew the curtains closed
   _____.
   A. two
   B. too
   C. to

3. Ann _____ to reflect on her two children to soothe her weary head.
   A. choose
   B. chosen
   C. chose

4. She took some pillows from a chair near the window, and _____ her aching feet to a slight elevation.
   A. rose
   B. raise
   C. raised

5. An old brown teddy bear with a plaid vest _____ on the pillow beside her.
   A. sat
   B. sit
   C. sitted

6. With most of its fur worn quite thin, it appeared to be _____ loved.
   A. special
   B. especially
   C. specially

7. While she rested, she thought about the _____ Mary had given her.
   A. advise
   B. advice
   C. advices

8. The wise words would prove to greatly _____ the final outcome.
   A. affect
   B. effect
   C. afect

9. If she wanted to get any _____ with her request, she should rethink her stategy.
   A. farther
   B. further
   C. father

10. She loosened her _____ for more comfort.
    A. cloths
    B. close
    C. clothes

11. All _____ the afternoon she tried to convince the committee of her son's needs.
    A. through
    B. threw
    C. though

12. They all asked her more medical questions _____ she had anticipated.
    A. than
    B. then
    C. ten

13. The chairperson also refused to _____ her request for nursing care.
    A. axcept
    B. except
    C. accept

14. While speaking with Mary over coffee, the chairperson agreed with Mary's wise _____ about obtaining written recommendations from the physicians.
    A. council
    B. counsel
    C. consul

15. Finally, with the peace and _____ of the early evening, she fell asleep.
    A. quiet
    B. quite
    C. quit

Exercise B

Choose the answer (A, B, or C) that correctly fills the blank.

1. What _____ will this rain have on your picnic plans?
    A. affect
    B. effect
    C. except

2. The band members will march _____ the principal's box seat.
    A. past
    B. passed
    C. pass

3. Stan's _____ never bothers him, no matter what he does.
    A. conscience
    B. conscious
    C. conscientious

4. Paula and Rico's new car is parked over _____.
    A. they're
    B. their
    C. there

5. She searched in _____ for her wallet.
    A. vein
    B. vain
    C. vane

6. _____ welcome in our house any time.
    A. Your
    B. You're
    C. You

7. I do not feel that I ought to _____ that money.
    A. except
    B. accept
    C. affect

8. The things _____ able to do around the house are not easy.
    A. you're
    B. yore
    C. your

9. Anyone _____ not part of the solution is part of the problem.
    A. whom
    B. whose
    C. who's

10. Joann asked the salesman for an itemized _____
    A. recite
    B. receit
    C. receipt

11. Scott loves strawberry cheesecake for _____ .
    A. desert
    B. dessert
    C. disert

12. Henry VIII's _____ was filled with bloodshed and turmoil.
    A. reign
    B. rain
    C. rein

13. After work, Debra always _____ down for a short nap
    A. lyes
    B. lies
    C. lays

14. James received legal _____ after his car accident.
    A. consul
    B. council
    C. counsel

15. Carla _____ her bookbag on the window seat by the front door.
    A. sat
    B. sit
    C. set

Exercise C

Choose the answer (A, B, or C) that correctly fills the blank or blanks.

1. Training at competitive sports is very challenging; however, dedicated athletes seldom
    _____.
    A. quiet
    B. quite
    C. quit

2. All the effort and hard work often seem to a winner to be her most _____ triumph.
    A. personal
    B. personnel
    C. personality

3. A focused athlete knows that only _____ dedicated training can she succeed.
    A. threw
    B. through
    C. thorough

4. Only when she's confident that she put forth her total effort is her _____ clear.
    A. conscientious
    B. conscious
    C. conscience

5. _____ really a matter of desire, persistence, and concentration.
    A. Its
    B. It's
    C. Its'

6. Even if she were to _____, just getting the competitive exposure is crucial to a beginning
    athlete.
    A. loose
    B. louse
    C. lose

7. For the younger athletes, in just working through the competitive circuit, _____ building
    early patterns of disciplined competitive behaviors.
    A. their
    B. there
    C. they're

8. Good sportsmanship is just as important as performing well; responsible athletes learn
    there is a _____ way to act among fellow competitors.
    A. rite
    B. write
    C. right

9. For almost any competitor it is painful to _____ defeat.
   A. accept
   B. axcept
   C. except

10. However, a true winner can _____ to be gracious in times of loss.
    A. choose
    B. choice
    C. chose

11. A well-admired runner reveals this to her readers in the _____ of her recent book.
    A. foreword
    B. forward
    C. fourword

12. A true champion's grace and character _____ her form and speed.
    A. compliment
    B. complement
    C. complimentary

13. Spectators love when an official _____ the gold medal to an athlete who demonstrates all the true virtues of a champion.
    A. presence
    B. prezents
    C. presents

14. Displaying graceful dignity when a fellow competitor takes the victory is one of the important _____ of passage for an athlete.
    A. rights
    B. rites
    C. writes

15. Participation and competition are _____ the biggest achievement _____.
    A. we're, lay
    B. where, lies
    C. wear, lays

Exercise D

Correct the words in the paragraph that use the wrong form.

Chicago has quiet an interesting history. The first Europeans came their about 1673. In

1779, Jean Baptiste Point du Sable, who's origins were from Haiti, built the first

permanent settlement. This was the beginning of one of our principle cities. In 1803,

Fort Dearborn was built on the sight. The fort was destroyed during the War of 1812 but

rebuilt in 1816. Chicago officially became a city in 1837. We do not know exactly where

the name "Chicago" comes from, but aural tradition among area Indian tribes reveal that

the word was used to mean "great" in describing the Mississippi River. One hundred

years ago, Chicago use to be a major railroad center. Today its still a great capitol of

commerce. People go thorough Chicago to get to many other destinations in the country.

Exercise E

Correct the words in the paragraph that use the wrong form.

Michael was more worried then his classmates about his grade in English. He did not want to loose any time, so he went to the tutoring center for help. Their he was counciled by the head tutor, who encouraged him not to waist any time. Michael kept a weekly appointment and wrote a hole essay each time he met with his tutor. He found that the work he was doing in his coarse improved while he was in the tutoring center, and he was much farther along in his writing because he never missed a session. He did very well on his final exam; all of his extra work was not in vane. Michael found that persistence was a big part of the receipt for success.

Exercise F

Correct the words in the paragraph that use the wrong form.

The principle airport in my country is located in a valley surrounded by mountains. The cite is said to be one of the most dangerous areas for landing a plain. In the passed, to many small aircraft use to take off in less then ideal conditions. Today, few pilots chose to take off in bad whether, and aircraft are usually stationery in times of severe storms.

Mastery Test

Choose whether A or B has the correct forms of the underlined words.

1. A. <u>Its</u> the choice of the management <u>weather</u> or not employees wear uniforms.
    B. <u>It's</u> the choice of the management <u>whether</u> or not employees wear uniforms.

2. A. <u>There</u> the ones who <u>past</u> us in the street today.
    B. <u>They're</u> the ones who <u>passed</u> us in the street today.

3. A. Of <u>coarse</u>, we could debate which <u>close</u> are most suitable.
    B. Of <u>course</u>, we could debate which <u>clothes</u> are most suitable.

4. A. The investigation of the crash <u>site</u> was <u>thorough</u>.
    B. The investigation of the crash <u>cite</u> was <u>through</u>.

5. A. <u>Except</u> for the cat, <u>whose</u> meows were heard from the garage, all the animals seemed content.
    B. <u>Accept</u> for the cat, <u>who's</u> meows were heard from the garage, all the animals seemed content.

6. A. I must <u>complement</u> you on the most dignified way <u>you're</u> dog waits for his meal.
    B. I must <u>compliment</u> you on the most dignified way <u>your</u> dog waits for his meal.

7. A. In her recommendation letter, written on ivory <u>stationery</u>, she <u>cites</u> many examples of her student's abilities.
    B. In her recommendation letter, written on ivory <u>stationary</u>, she <u>sights</u> many examples of her student's abilities.

8. A. <u>Through</u> the fog, Peter thought he could make out the <u>presence</u> of a large structure.
    B. <u>Threw</u> the fog, Peter thought he could make out the <u>presents</u> of a large structure.

9. A. During a short break in the conversation, the <u>quiet</u> boy ate his <u>dessert</u>.
    B. During a short break in the conversation, the <u>quite</u> boy ate his <u>desert</u>.

10. A. I shall look <u>forward</u> to the day I write the <u>foreword</u> to the book.
    B. I shall look <u>foreword</u> to the day I write the <u>forward</u> to the book.

Answers

Finding Subjects and Verbs in Simple Sentences (p. 02)

Diagnostic Test (p. 2)

1. B
2. A
3. C
4. A
5. C
6. C
7. A
8. C
9. A
10. C

Exercise A (p. 3)

1. cheetah
2. speed
3. legs
4. shoulder blades
5. nostrils (and) airway
6. lungs
7. claws
8. claws
9. feature
10. pad

Exercise B (p. 4)

1. B
2. C
3. C
4. C
5. A
6. A
7. C
8. B
9. A
10. A
11. B
12. B
13. C
14. B
15. A

Exercise C (p. 6)

<u>Miami</u>, a city with miles of beaches amid many high-priced neighborhoods, <u>is</u> my hometown. With an average of 359 days of sunshine every year, <u>it</u> <u>has become</u> a leading winter resort. Not surprisingly, <u>tourism</u> <u>continues</u> to be the largest source of income.

In the 1960s and in 1980, large <u>numbers</u> of Cubans <u>immigrated</u> to Miami. The <u>city</u> now <u>has</u> the largest Cuban community in the United States. The <u>flavor</u> of the Latin American culture <u>adds</u> to the charm of the city. In addition to tourism, the <u>metropolis</u> <u>holds</u> a place of importance as a business and financial center. This <u>port</u> of entry <u>is</u> a terminal for the vast air and sea trade with Latin America. Many business and financial <u>firms</u> <u>have</u> their headquarters in Miami. My fondest <u>memories</u> of Miami <u>will</u> always <u>be</u> of the days sunning, picnicing, and playing Frisbee on the beach.

Exercise D (p. 7)

The most common <u>type</u> of giraffe <u>is</u> the reticulated giraffe. Its <u>colors</u> <u>have</u> a clear pattern of white lines surrounding the darker brown spots. With their speed, adult <u>animals</u> <u>are</u> relatively safe from predators. Additionally, the giraffe's large <u>hooves</u> also <u>help</u> in its defense. A <u>kick</u> from an adult giraffe <u>can be</u> deadly for predators as fierce as lions. However, in order to drink, the <u>giraffe</u> <u>must lower</u> its head down to the water. To do this, the <u>giraffe</u> <u>spreads</u> its long legs to lower itself. In this position, the <u>giraffe</u> <u>is</u> vulnerable to attack.

Exercise E (p. 8)

At the spring recital, the young <u>pianist</u> <u>performed</u> Beethoven's "Moonlight Sonata." The <u>audience</u> <u>remained</u> motionless. In the dark concert hall, there <u>was</u> not even the <u>rustling</u> of a program. The <u>soloist</u> <u>sat</u> alone in the spotlight on the stage. The young <u>man</u> <u>was</u> a first year student from New York. His <u>entrance</u> to the music academy <u>had depended</u> on a scholarship. His <u>interpretation</u> of Beethoven's music then <u>had</u> <u>impressed</u> his masters. Now <u>they</u> also <u>remarked</u> on the emotional intensity of his performance. At the end of the sonata, <u>he</u> <u>stood, turned</u>, and <u>bowed</u> to the audience. The thunderous <u>applause</u> <u>lit</u> up his boyish face.

Exercise F (p. 9)

<u>I</u> <u>love</u> movies, especially comedies. <u>Movies</u> <u>can take</u> me to other countries or other times. <u>*Robin Hood: Men in Tights*</u>, one of Mel Brooks' films, <u>is</u> one of my favorites and <u>features</u> Cary Elwes and Richard Lewis. At Christmas, <u>I</u> <u>enjoy</u> watching *Scrooged* with Bill Murray. <u>Bill Murray</u> <u>plays</u> the Ebenezer Scrooge part. <u>He</u> <u>is</u> a television executive. Romantic <u>comedies</u>, like *When Harry Met Sally*, and *Roxanne*, <u>represent</u> another category of my favorites. <u>*When Harry Met Sally*</u>, featuring Billy Crystal and Meg Ryan, <u>chronicles</u> a couple's romantic journey to the altar. <u>Steve Martin</u> with a huge fake nose <u>is</u> the star of *Roxanne*, a modern day Cyrano de Bergerac. <u>Everyone</u> <u>needs</u> a good laugh. <u>Laughing</u> <u>makes</u> me feel less stressed.

Mastery Test (p. 10)

1. B
2. B
3. A
4. C
5. A

6. B
7. C
8. C
9. C
10. A

Making Subjects and Verbs Agree (p. 11)

Diagnostic Test (p. 11)

1. B
2. A
3. B
4. B (the group act as individuals—"they")
5. A
6. B
7. B
8. A (the group acts as a unit—"it")
9. A
10. B

Exercise A (p. 12)

1. A
2. A
3. A
4. A
5. B
6. B
7. A
8. B
9. B
10. A

Exercise B (p. 13)

1. A
2. A
3. B
4. A
5. A
6. A
7. B
8. A
9. B
10. B
11. B
12. A
13. B
14. A
15. B

Exercise C (p. 15)

1. A
2. A
3. B
4. B
5. A
6. B
7. B
8. A
9. A
10. A
11. B
12. B
13. A
14. A
15. A

Exercise D (p. 17)

1. B
2. B
3. A
4. A
5. B
6. B
7. B
8. A
9. B
10. B
11. A
12. B
13. B
14. A
15. B

Exercise E (p. 18)

Montreal, the City of Festivals, (is, are) alive with street parties and celebrations. The people of Montreal (ranks, rank) high among the world's supporters of urban festivals. Festivals such as the Annual Jazz Fest and the World Film Festival (accounts, account) for just a few. A crowd (gathers, gather) at the appearance of a street band. A pair of comfortable shoes (is, are) essential for anyone touring historic Old Montreal. Everybody (finds, find) something to enjoy in Montreal's dining establishments. These restaurants, cafes, and bistros (offers, offer) the cuisine of several nationalities. At the Biodome de Montreal, visitors (explores, explore) re-creations of natural ecosystems. The Botanical Garden, with over thirty gardens, (is, are) a popular touring site. Montreal's chic boulevards and 18-mile Underground City (delights, delight) shoppers.

Exercise F (p. 19)

Each of the committee members (<u>works</u>, work) the whole afternoon to get ready for the dance. Everyone in the group (<u>has</u>, have) a different task. There (<u>is</u>, are) so much to be done before the class arrives. The committee chairperson (<u>doesn't</u>, don't) feel confident. However, the members on the committee (keeps, <u>keep</u>) up the pace to turn the gym into a dance hall. The sound and the lights (is, <u>are</u>) checked. Streamers and banners (adds, <u>add</u>) color and design to the pale blue walls of the gym. (Does, <u>Do</u>) the banners announce the special occasion? "The Spring Fling" banner, painted in pastels, (<u>stretches</u>, stretch) across the far wall. Who (is, <u>are</u>) the artists of such beautiful artwork?

Mastery Test (p. 20)

1. B
2. B
3. A
4. B
5. A
6. B
7. A
8. A
9. B
10. A

Understanding Fragments and Phrases (p. 21)

Diagnostic Test (p. 21)

1. B
2. C
3. D
4. E
5. B
6. A
7. F
8. A
9. B
10. C

Exercise A (p. 22)

1. A
2. E
3. D
4. C
5. B
6. C
7. E
8. B
9. F
10. B
11. B

12. B
13. A
14. C
15. E

Exercise B (p. 23)

1. B
2. C
3. A
4. D
5. D
6. B
7. A
8. D
9. B
10. C

Exercise C (p. 24)

1. B
2. A
3. A
4. A
5. C
6. A
7. B
8. A
9. A
10. D
11. C
12. A
13. A
14. C
15. B

Exercise D (p. 25)

1. A
2. B
3. B
4. B
5. B
6. A
7. A
8. C
9. D
10. D
11. B
12. A
13. B
14. D
15. C

Exercise E (p. 26)

1. D
2. D
3. D
4. A
5. B
6. B
7. D
8. A
9. C
10. B
11. A
12. A
13. A
14. A
15. D

Exercise F (p. 27)

Answers may vary.

1. The mountain climber is on top of the mountain.
2. Stopping me, the traveler needed directions.
3. Sue was wearing a red scarf around her neck.
4. The food should be kept in the refrigerator.
5. The book is easy to read.
6. I wanted to help.
7. The baseball has been placed in the display case.
8. I did not see the ice.
9. He was dressed all in green.
10. The old fashioned ice cream social was held on Sunday.

Exercise G (p. 29)

Answers may vary.

Understanding the very basic science of leaf coloration can make observation more interesting. The gradual, but quite dazzling, color changes among the leaves of deciduous trees like oaks, hickories, sumacs, maples, aspens, and gums occur only in America's temperate zones. Among these areas, the display in the East is especially brilliant in its colors of autumn foliage. Exceptionally breathtaking views can be seen by travelers on New England roadway tours. These tours are known for the fiery red sugar maples. This incredible backdrop of color has impressed vacationers for countless autumn seasons.

Mastery Test (p. 30)

Answers may vary.

1. We ought to be in line today.
2. The young man, with time off from work, went to the ticket office.

3. He wants to purchase tickets.
4. He loves hockey.
5. They have a new center and a new point guard.
6. The coach begins practice on Tuesday.
7. The season ticket holders get to sit in the best seats.
8. The others watch from the seats in the upper deck.
9. We will try for the best tickets.
10. The refreshment stand sells pizza and soft drinks.

Combining Sentences Using Three Options for Coordination (p. 32)

Diagnostic Test (p. 32)

1. C
2. A
3. A
4. B
5. B
6. C
7. B
8. B
9. C
10. A

Exercise A (p. 34)

1. C
2. B
3. B
4. B
5. A
6. C
7. A
8. A
9. A
10. A
11. B
12. C
13. C
14. A
15. A

Exercise B (p. 36)

1. A
2. B
3. B
4. C
5. C
6. B
7. B

8. C
9. B
10. C
11. B
12. C
13. A
14. A
15. A

Exercise C (p. 38)

1. C
2. B
3. B
4. C
5. C
6. A
7. B
8. A
9. C
10. C
11. C
12. A
13. B
14. A
15. C

Exercise D (p. 40)

1. B
2. A
3. C
4. A
5. A
6. B
7. C
8. B
9. C
10. A
11. B
12. C
13. A
14. B
15. B

Exercise E (p. 42)

Answers may vary.

1. Dinner was late, but the food was great.
2. The earrings were of base metal, but the other jewelry was 14K gold.
3. Barney made reservations at the local steak house, for he had his mother-in-law to impress.

4. Friday is my favorite day of the week, for I always go out to dinner and a movie.
5. The professional photographer took pictures, and the relatives took pictures.

Exercise F (p. 43)

Answers may vary. This is one possible answer.

1. The box was not in the trunk, nor was it on the backseat.
2. Maria's brother did not sleep, so he was grumpy the next morning.
3. Scott went to Costa Rica, for he wanted to surf in a new place.
4. Laddie, our dog, is a German shepherd, and Mittens, our cat, is a Siamese.
5. Jeremy might go to the football game, or he might stay home.

Exercise G (p. 44)

In the Arizona desert, the Saguaro cactus is a unique plant; <u>nevertheless</u>, it is being maimed and stolen. Not only is the Saguaro the largest species of cactus in the United States, <u>but</u> it also takes hundreds of years to grow. Believe it or not, every week people use the Saguaro as target practice. Perhaps these gunmen don't realize the damage they are causing, <u>or</u> even worse perhaps they don't care. One bullet can stop decades of growing. Another problem is the theft of these cacti. It is very desirable to have a big Saguaro with its many arms in a yard in Arizona; <u>consequently</u>, many people dig them up and sell them to homeowners. These gunmen and poachers must be stopped; <u>otherwise</u>, these beautiful symbols of the Wild West will disappear from the landscape.

Exercise H (p. 45)

Some artists use paint or clay to create their art; <u>instead</u>, Arthur S. Mole used people. He created group photographs; <u>however</u>, you could not see the individual people. He arranged tens of thousands of people with different colored shirts; <u>the effect</u> was a patriotic American image. Back when he worked, around 1918, patriotism was very popular. World War I had just ended, <u>and</u> people wanted to express their enthusiasm for winning the war. Mole would organize troops into formations, like a portrait of Woodrow Wilson, a U.S. shield, the Statue of Liberty, or the Liberty Bell. President Woodrow Wilson was impressed with the photograph of his portrait; <u>indeed</u>, he signed it with a flourish.

Mastery Test (p. 46)

1. C
2. A
3. B
4. A
5. C
6. C
7. C
8. A
9. C
10. A

Combining Sentences using Subordination (p. 47)

Diagnostic Test (p. 47)

1. A
2. B
3. A
4. A
5. C
6. A
7. C
8. Jayne, with whom I am eating lunch, is in my next class.
9. The French horn that Zanetta plays is an antique.
10. My doctor, whose office is decorated with a jungle motif, will be on vacation next week.

Exercise A (p. 49)

1. B
2. B
3. A
4. B
5. A
6. B
7. A
8. B
9. B
10. A
11. B
12. B
13. A
14. B
15. B

Exercise B (p. 51)

1. A
2. B
3. A
4. B
5. B
6. A
7. B
8. A
9. B
10. A
11. B
12. B
13. B
14. B
15. A

Exercise C (p. 53)

1. B
2. A
3. A
4. C
5. B
6. A
7. B
8. C
9. A
10. A

Exercise D (p. 54)

1. A
2. C
3. A
4. B
5. A
6. B
7. C
8. A
9. A
10. B

Exercise E (p. 56)

Answers may vary.

1. Tropical plants will not flourish unless you provide them with water, nutrients, and light.
2. Although tropical plants grow naturally in warmer climates, people in colder places can enjoy them indoors during the autumn and winter months.
3. If tropical plants are kept under ideal conditions, some species will even flower, adding to their beauty.
4. Provided that they are taken inside before the first cold air of autumn comes, tropical plants can be put outside for an extra boost.
5. Wherever they are placed in the home, tropical plants add beautiful color and texture.
6. The concert hall, which has now grown silent, is filled to capacity.
7. That violinist, who is the youngest orchestra member, is the concertmaster.
8. The older members, who await his entrance, have great respect for him.
9. The young concertmaster, whose artistry is matched by his graciousness, is a favorite among Philadelphia audiences.
10. The young man's mother, who lives in Chicago, has come to see her son's debut.

Exercise F (p. 58)

1. We went to London <u>because</u> we wanted to see Big Ben.
2. Orlando agreed to go on the trip <u>provided that</u> he could visit his friend afterwards.
3. His charisma carried him through the presentation <u>even though</u> he didn't know much about the topic.
4. <u>Since</u> my aunt moved away, life hasn't been the same.

5. <u>If</u> Shirley wants to drive, we can go into the city tonight.
6. The garden, <u>whose</u> trees blocked the hot midday sun, was a perfect retreat.
7. Good soil, <u>which</u> is hard to find in this area, must be created.
8. Frank Lloyd Wright, <u>who</u> designed the Guggenheim Museum, was a noted architect.
9. The Atlanta Botanical Garden, <u>which</u> is located on Piedmont Avenue, is a volunteer-run garden.
10. The title of Hemingway's *For Whom the Bell Tolls* comes from the poem, "No Man Is an Island," <u>whose</u> author is John Donne.

Exercise G (p. 60)

Answers may vary. This is one possible revision.

> <u>As</u> John was sleeping beneath the warm army blanket, the radio alarm cut in with the morning weather and travel advisory. The storm had arrived just as predicted. John jumped up from his warm covers <u>even though</u> the room was cold. He is like so many road workers <u>who</u> secretly enjoy the challenge of a snowstorm. <u>Although</u> bed is warm and comfortable, John's sense of duty wins out. In the predawn, snowdrifts cover the city streets. Without plowing, morning traffic would be at a standstill. John and the rest of the snow removal crew arrive with giant plows. <u>After</u> the plows push the snow to the sides, intersections are sanded or covered with rock salt. Few commuters will be delayed <u>when</u> they start off for work at 8:00 AM.

Exercise H (p. 61)

Answers may vary.

1. Bob Hope, who was 100 years old when he died in 2003, was in vaudeville, radio, and movies.
2. Hope was born in 1903 in England and moved to Cleveland, Ohio, when he was four.
3. Hope, who was originally Leslie Townes Hope, changed his name when he became an entertainer.
4. Although Bob Hope appeared in over seventy movies, he is most famous for performing in hundreds of USO programs, which he started during World War II.
5. Hope, who was named an honorary military veteran in 1997 by President Clinton, performed in shows in Europe, Japan, South Korea, Vietnam, and the Persian Gulf.
6. Kelsey Grammer, who is one of Hope's biggest fans, hosted a television special honoring Hope on his 100th birthday.

Exercise I (p. 63)

1. A
2. B
3. B
4. A
5. B
6. A
7. A
8. A
9. A
10. A

Mastery Test (p. 64)

1. B
2. A
3. B
4. C
5. B
6. C
7. C
8. A
9. B
10. C

Correcting Fragments and Run-ons (p. 66)

Diagnostic Test (p. 66)

1. B
2. A
3. A
4. B
5. C
6. Mr. Nye has spent most of his adult life trying to save bald eagles from extinction, and he has nursed hundreds of eaglets.
7. He is the man who is in charge of one of the most successful reintroduction programs in the country.
8. Eagles have been seen this past winter on ice floes in the Hudson River near the George Washington Bridge; furthermore, one Audubon member reported seeing an eagle flying over Grant's tomb.
9. When Mr. Nye started in the 1970s, a bald eagle was a rare sight.
10. In 1970, there was only one known nesting pair of eagles in New York State, but today there are 75 pairs.

Exercise A (p. 68)

1. B
2. A
3. A
4. B
5. B
6. A
7. A
8. B
9. B
10. A

Exercise B (p. 69)

1. A
2. A
3. B
4. A

5. B
6. A
7. B
8. A
9. B
10. A

Exercise C (p. 70)

1. A
2. C
3. C
4. A
5. C
6. B
7. B
8. C
9. B
10. A

Exercise D (p. 71)

1. C
2. B
3. A
4. B
5. C
6. A
7. C
8. B
9. C
10. B
11. A
12. C
13. C
14. C
15. B

Exercise E (p. 73)

1. A
2. C
3. A
4. C
5. A
6. B
7. A
8. C
9. B
10. A
11. B
12. A
13. A

14. C
15. B

Exercise F (p. 75)

1. A
2. C
3. B
4. C
5. A
6. C
7. B
8. A
9. B
10. B
11. A
12. B
13. A
14. A
15. C

Exercise G (p. 77)

1. B
2. A
3. C
4. A
5. A
6. C
7. B
8. C
9. B
10. C

Exercise H (p. 79)

1. B
2. A
3. B
4. A
5. C
6. B
7. A
8. A
9. A
10. C

Mastery Test (p. 81)

1. B
2. A
3. B
4. A

   5. B
   6. A
   7. A
   8. B
   9. A
  10. B

Making Sentence Parts Work Together (p. 83)

Diagnostic Test (p. 83)

   1. C
   2. B
   3. C
   4. C
   5. A
   6. A
   7. B
   8. B
   9. C
  10. A

Part I: Pronouns (p. 85)

Exercise A (p. 85)

   1. A
   2. A
   3. B
   4. A
   5. A
   6. A
   7. B
   8. A
   9. B
  10. A
  11. B
  12. A
  13. B
  14. B
  15. A

Exercise B (p. 87)

   1. A
   2. A
   3. A
   4. B
   5. B
   6. A
   7. B
   8. A

9. B
10. A
11. A
12. B
13. B
14. A
15. B

Exercise C (p. 89)

1. A
2. B
3. A
4. A
5. A
6. A
7. B
8. A
9. B
10. A
11. A
12. A
13. B
14. A
15. B

Exercise D (p. 91)

1. Eating chocolate is <u>Evan's</u> passion; <u>he</u> has chocolate every night.

2. The <u>restaurant</u> provides napkins and plastic forks and knives for all <u>its</u> takeout customers.

3. My best friend, <u>Michelle</u>, <u>who</u> is getting married in July, is very beautiful in <u>her</u> wedding dress.

4. <u>Sharon</u> knows that <u>her</u> grandmother will be here today.

5. <u>Paper and pens</u> are available in the bookstore, and <u>they</u> are reasonably priced.

6. Although <u>he</u> agreed to help, <u>Geoff</u> was regretting the decision.

7. The <u>football game</u> went into overtime; the network decided to keep airing <u>it</u>.

8. <u>Susan and Maria</u> went to the mall because <u>they</u> wanted to buy new bathing suits.

9. The five <u>students</u> were finishing <u>their</u> tests.

10. <u>Meg, Dirk, and Tonya</u> were the first to be invited, but <u>they</u> were not the only ones.

11. A colorful <u>parachute</u> opened to <u>its</u> full size in the wind.

12. <u>Everyone</u> had <u>his or her</u> own calculator today.

13.   Lamar tried on the latest basketball <u>shoes</u>; however, <u>they</u> were not comfortable.

14.   The <u>book</u> <u>that</u> Neil had was a classic.

15.   Move the <u>chairs</u> so <u>they</u> make even rows.

Exercise E (p. 92)

1.   A
2.   C
3.   B
4.   B
5.   C
6.   A
7.   B
8.   A
9.   C
10.   C
11.   A
12.   B
13.   C
14.   A
15.   C

Part II: Parallel Structure and Modifiers (p. 94)

Exercise F (p. 94)

1.   Tourists to Tennessee can go to Nashville, Chattanooga, or Memphis.
2.   If you are taking a class that is difficult, you should either get help from the instructor or go to the tutoring center.
3.   Cats are smart, flexible, and aloof.
4.   In the movies, actors can be dramatic, funny, or both.
5.   Either the couch or the recliner is my favorite spot to watch television.
6.   Beale Street in Memphis has enjoyed a rebirth in its tourist business because of the emphasis on cleanliness, safety, and new businesses.
7.   Fish, shrimp, and clams are my main reasons for eating at the shore.
8.   Damien likes swimming, driving his motorcycle, and watching movies.
9.   Crocheting baby booties, knitting sweaters, and making cakes are my mother's favorite hobbies.
10.   The tires have to be rotated, the oil needs to be changed, and new windshield wipers need to be installed.
11.   Sebastian's homework is on his computer desk, under his bed, or in his car.
12.   Arabian camels have one hump; Bactrian camels have two humps.
13.   Blue whales are over eighty feet long, have a heart as big as a Volkswagon Beetle, and weigh 150 tons.
14.   Danielle loves to read, and Sam loves to swim.
15.   The winds blew, the temperature dropped, and rain lashed at the windows.

Exercise G (p. 96)

1.   The bathroom had tile on the floor, on the wall behind the sink, and in the shower stall.
2.   Serena was sassy, happy, and energetic.

3. Being secretive and keeping quiet are traits of a good lawyer.
4. Armando left his car in the parking lot, under a shady tree, and in a legal space.
5. The mystery show has all the right ingredients: a tantalizing story, interesting characters, and a showdown in the courtroom.
6. For the scavenger hunt, Bill had on a Florida Gators hat, extra stuffing in his shirt, and a newspaper hiding his face.
7. The remote control is usually on the coffee table, in the basket, or between the cushions.
8. Singing, dancing, and acting are Julio's passions.
9. The chair is made of maple, glue, and nails.
10. Orange juice, chicken soup, and a nap are good ways to get over a cold.
11. Jackie wants to learn how to quilt, to sew, and to cook French dishes.
12. As the clouds moved in and the wind blew, Keith knew it would be cold tomorrow.
13. The man walked down the street, across the park, and to his car.
14. Strategies for getting better grades include taking notes, reading closely, and reviewing regularly.
15. During the day, cardinals chirped in the apple trees, but at night, an old owl hooted in the oak tree out back.

Exercise H (p. 98)

Answers may vary. These are possible answers.

1. While I talked on the cell phone, the cat curled around my feet.
2. Rick was feeling good after he had spent a day in bed.
3. Lisa made the most delicious spaghetti Dave had ever tasted.
4. When I was thirteen, my parents moved our family to Cleveland.
5. The lawyers on television advertisements simply want you to choose them.
6. While Doug paid the veterinarian's bill, the dog pulled on the leash Doug was holding.
7. Peter scarcely had enough money to pay his bill.
8. Tanya caught up with her teenage son who had been skateboarding all day.
9. Watching the sunset at dinner, I would indulge in a giant lobster tail.
10. Trudy almost became a nurse.
11. After I had been gone for three months, the school looked just the same.
12. I thought my husband looked handsome dressed in a dark blue tuxedo.
13. Jolene's house where she was born is near the Grand Canyon.
14. My mother started me on violin lessons when I was four.
15. While I was swimming in shallow water, my ankle scraped a rock.

Exercise I (p. 100)

Answers may vary. These are possible answers.

1. The woman gazed hungrily at the candy bar.
2. Sergio was the better of the two runners.
3. Since I had not eaten for hours, the sandwich looked delicious.
4. The new job in Atlanta, Georgia, would be a challenge.
5. After we took the exam, the results were calculated.
6. The Overseas Highway, which is 106 miles long, is the only way to the Florida Keys.
7. Last year, my sister bought a car with no backseat from a friend.
8. After the first of the year, Jack's company wants to hire an accountant who will be more efficient.
9. After I washed the car, my dog wanted to be walked.
10. Mike saw his gym shorts hanging from the flagpole.

11. We saw the mountains while we were flying over Colorado.
12. When I was five, my father got a new job, and we moved to Chicago.
13. While Jan was on vacation, her house was robbed.
14. I was excited about my vacation, and the plane took off soon after I boarded it.
15. I eat almost anything pickled.

Exercise J (p. 102)

Answers may vary.

The decision to become full-time, stay-at-home mothers and housewives used to be made for them. Pregnant women who worked always quit their jobs just before having their babies. Family situations are different in our society today. As more and more families are requiring two incomes, this traditional family arrangement is not always the case. Some women are keeping their jobs after delivery, some are scaling back to part-time, and some are participating in job sharing. While many women view themselves as the primary parents responsible for care of their babies, there are some men, whose wives may have the larger salaries, who decide to stay home. With both parents carefully considering what is best for them, babies in non-traditional homes are fortunate to experience different styles of care often administered by fathers. Clearly, whatever the arrangement, parenting roles today are no longer gender specific.

Exercise K (p. 103)

Answers may vary. These are possible answers.

New parents who decide to use daycare for their children must also decide on the specific daycare setting. Some children benefit from a surrounding that is socially stimulating, which means it contains other children and maybe a number of caregivers. Some parents of shy children say they can help their children more by exposing them to other children. On the other hand, parents sometimes believe their individual child would benefit more from a more intimate one-on-one care situation, in which the caregiver cares for only the one child. Whether the child attends a daycare center or stays home with his or her home caregiver, the quality of care is the issue. Any caregiver, whether working in a center or in a home, should be warm, compassionate, and encouraging.

Exercise L (p. 104)

Answers may vary. These are possible answers.

When a new parent, who must work, lives near his or her parents, another childcare option becomes available. Children cared for by enthusiastic grandparents can have the advantage of feeling a genuine love that can significantly strengthen the bond between caregiver and child. Of course, this arrangement doesn't work optimally in all situations. Indeed, certain characteristics must be present for the situation to work for all people involved. This is, basically, that parent should respect grandparent and grandparent should respect parent. The most significant benefit that can come from such a childcare situation is an unconditional love for the child, which sometimes can only come from family members. This is not to mention the added benefit of monetary savings since childcare is so expensive.

Exercise M (p. 105)

Answers may vary. These are possible answers.

Can you remember details about where you were, what <u>you were</u> doing, or <u>whom</u> you were with when the Challenger exploded? People often have vivid recollections of when <u>they</u> heard some important news. <u>This is called</u> "flashbulb memory." You remember everything <u>exactly</u> as it went on around you when you heard about a striking event. You may think your flashbulb memory is very accurate; however, <u>studies show</u> that it may not be. Time may make you forget certain things. <u>Conflicting details may make your recollection change.</u> You may want to remember the event differently, so you convince yourself that events happened differently. Flashbulb memory may not be that detailed, precise, or <u>accurate</u>.

Mastery Test (p. 106)

1. B
2. A
3. A
4. C
5. C
6. C
7. B
8. A
9. B
10. B

Practicing More with Verbs (p. 107)

Diagnostic Test (p. 107)

1. C
2. B
3. A
4. C
5. B
6. C
7. B
8. A
9. A
10. B

Exercise A (p. 109)

1. A
2. C
3. A
4. A
5. C
6. A
7. B
8. A

9. A
10. C
11. C
12. C
13. A
14. C
15. B

Exercise B (p. 111)

1. A
2. A
3. A
4. B
5. C
6. B
7. A
8. A
9. C
10. C
11. B
12. A
13. A
14. A
15. A

Exercise C (p. 113)

1. P The party guests enjoyed the buffet.
2. A The notes were taken at the meeting by Sally.
3. A In the train station, the train was waited for by the people.
4. P The other workers helped Will, the assistant manager.
5. P Marva made delicious iced tea.
6. P The wind blew the branches.
7. A Gina was given a pair of earrings by her husband, Gene.
8. A Homework was given to the class by the teacher.
9. A Maria and Sonya were waved to by Tim, emerging from his car.
10. P The movie star made a grand entrance.
11. P Linda rebooted the computers.
12. P Last fall, a record number of people watched football.
13. P A teenage driver ran over the trash cans in front of Bob's house.
14. A During the car accident, Julie was protected by the seatbelt.
15. A On Thursday, at least one hundred flu shots were given by the nurses.

Exercise D (p. 115)

That gloomy night, an angry wind <u>blew</u> so hard that the branches of the large oak tree tapped continually at his window. Soon, the small child was so frightened by the storm that he <u>crept</u> into his parents' room. As always, his parents had been soundly sleeping and <u>heard</u> nothing. As he <u>sat</u> quietly on the floor, by his mother's side of the bed, he <u>thought</u> he <u>saw</u> a large arm out <u>through</u> his parents' window. At once he <u>started</u> shivering. He then <u>crawled</u> into bed next to his mother, <u>closed</u> his eyes tight to shut it all out, and <u>awoke</u> finally to the morning sun <u>shining</u> brilliantly in the same sky that appeared so ominous the night before.

Exercise E (p. 116)

Ian Fleming's James Bond <u>has become</u> the most successful set of movie sequels, with twenty films total. Fleming <u>began</u> to write the books in 1952. In 1962, Harry Saltzman and Albert Cubby Broccoli <u>began</u> filming the books, beginning with *Dr. No*. Sean Connery <u>was chosen</u> as the first James Bond. In these movies, Bond always enjoyed the company of beautiful women. There <u>were</u> also various gadgets and fancy cars for Bond, too. Sean Connery <u>did</u> five movies before Roger Moore <u>took</u> over as James Bond. Moore made seven movies as James Bond. He <u>could have made</u> more, but he decided to retire. Timothy Dalton, David Niven, and George Lazenby <u>have each taken</u> a shot at Bond fame. The most recent Bond is Pierce Brosnan who has been in four Bond movies. Ian Fleming <u>would have been</u> proud of his secret agent.

Exercise F (p. 117)

1. Quickly close the door!
2. Does your mother have papers and projects from when you were in elementary school?
3. Websites that are about urban legends explain how each legend got started.
4. Everyone in the classes has written a paper for the contest.
5. When the alarm sounds, you should leave the building and meet in the designated place.
6. The young boys fought on the playground.
7. Have you heard that the new Harry Potter movie will soon be out?
8. What did Sharon have for breakfast?
9. Nestled in their beds, the children slept soundly.
10. Julian was mistaken for a criminal because he had the same kind of car.

Mastery Test (p. 119)

1. B
2. A
3. A
4. C
5. B
6. C
7. B
8. A
9. C
10. A

Using Correct Capitalization and Punctuation (p. 121)

Diagnostic Test (p. 121)

1. C
2. A
3. A
4. B
5. A

6.   B
7.   B
8.   A
9.   B
10. B

Exercise A (p. 122)

1.   B
2.   B
3.   A
4.   B
5.   B
6.   B
7.   A
8.   B
9.   B
10. A
11. B
12. B
13. A
14. B
15. A

Exercise B (p. 124)

1.   A
2.   B
3.   B
4.   B
5.   A
6.   B
7.   B
8.   A
9.   A
10. A
11. B
12. A
13. A
14. A
15. A

Exercise C (p. 126)

1.   B
2.   A
3.   A
4.   B
5.   B
6.   A
7.   B
8.   A

9. A
10. B
11. A
12. A
13. B
14. B
15. A

Exercise D (p. 127)

1. B
2. B
3. A
4. A
5. B
6. B
7. A
8. B
9. B
10. A
11. B
12. A
13. B
14. A
15. A

Exercise E (p. 128)

1. A
2. B
3. B
4. C
5. C
6. C
7. C
8. B
9. C
10. B

Exercise F (p. 130)

1. B
2. A
3. C
4. B
5. A
6. A
7. C
8. C
9. B
10. A
11. C

12. A
13. B
14. A
15. A

Exercise G (p. 133)

1. B
2. C
3. A
4. C
5. A
6. B
7. B
8. A
9. C
10. A
11. C
12. B
13. C
14. A
15. A

Exercise H (p. 135)

The Harlem Renaissance is noted for the resurgence of African American art. This art, which had already earned respect in Europe, finally found an open door here at home in the United States. Poets, writers, musicians, and intellectuals had found a place for themselves. In the New York of the 1920s, Harlem became a fertile cultural center that fostered and stimulated all forms of the arts. Musicians such as Duke Ellington, Louis Armstrong, and Eubie Blake, just to name a very few, joined their musical expression with the written expression of writers such as Langston Hughes, Dorothy West, Zora Neale Hurston, and Countee Cullen. Visual arts and theater depicted the political, social, and economic conditions of being black in America. The time period remains one of the most uplifting to African Americans as artists.

Exercise I (p. 136)

Answers may vary.

If I could be anywhere but here, where would I be? I would head south to Key West to visit my aunt and uncle, whom I haven't seen in a while. I enjoy spending time with them. My uncle is a professional fisherman, and my aunt is the best fish cook I know. Besides the family, I love the whole Jimmy Buffett life: sitting on the beach and listening to country music. Another reason I would want to be there is to go scuba diving. The water is one of the calmest places, at least under water. The best time is at night out in the middle of the ocean looking at the stars. That is where I would be if I could be anywhere but here.

Exercise J (p. 137)

<u>J.D.</u> Salinger was born Jerome David Salinger in <u>New York City</u> on <u>January 1,</u> 1919. He attended Valley Forge Military <u>A</u>cademy in Pennsylvania<u>, and</u> he graduated in 1936. After his draft into the United States <u>Army in 1942</u>, and discharge <u>in 1945,</u> he began publishing his short stories regularly in some of the bigger magazines<u>, including</u> the *Saturday Evening Post, Esquire,* and the *New Yorker.* His publishing career became most defined by a long relationship with the *New Yorker,* beginning in the late 1940s (or 1940's). <u>Then, in 1951,</u> his novel *The Catcher in the Rye* was published and became the work that Salinger is most well known for today.

Exercise K (p. 138)

Archimedes <u>(287–212 BC)</u> was a Greek <u>m</u>athematician and <u>i</u>nventor in the fields of <u>p</u>lane and <u>s</u>olid geometry, arithmetic, and basic mechanics. He was born in <u>S</u>yracuse, <u>Sicily,</u> but he was educated in Alexandria, Egypt, a center for <u>learning during</u> that time. While he was in <u>E</u>gypt<u>,</u> he invented the hydraulic screw for raising <u>water from</u> lower to higher levels. He also defined the <u>p</u>rinciples of the <u>lever and</u> invented the compound pulley. Living mostly in <u>Sicily, Archimedes</u> devoted his life to <u>research and</u> <u>e</u>xperiments. <u>He is</u> most famous for Archimedes' Principle which is the law of <u>h</u>ydrostatics. The <u>p</u>rinciple <u>states that</u> a body immersed in water loses weight equal to the amount of water it displaces. The story claims that Archimedes was taking a <u>bath</u> <u>when</u> he noticed the water splashing out of his tub. The catapult was another of <u>A</u>rchimedes' inventions. He also discovered that several properly placed mirrors could start fires on <u>R</u>oman ships that were attacking Sicily. Archimedes was a great <u>m</u>athematician<u>; he</u> was also a great inventor.

Mastery Test (p. 139)

1. B
2. C
3. C
4. A
5. A
6. B
7. A
8. B
9. C
10. A

Paying Attention to Look-Alikes and Sound-Alikes (p. 140)

Diagnostic Test (p. 140)

1. B
2. A
3. B
4. A
5. A
6. A

7. B
8. A
9. B
10. B

Exercise A (p. 141)

1. B
2. B
3. C
4. C
5. A
6. B
7. B
8. A
9. B
10. C
11. A
12. A
13. C
14. B
15. A

Exercise B (p. 143)

1. B
2. A
3. A
4. C
5. B
6. B
7. B
8. A
9. C
10. C
11. B
12. A
13. B
14. C
15. C

Exercise C (p. 145)

1. C
2. A
3. B
4. C
5. B
6. C
7. C
8. C

9.   A
10.   A
11.   A
12.   B
13.   C
14.   B
15.   B

Exercise D (p. 147)

Chicago has <u>quite</u> an interesting history. The first Europeans came <u>there</u> about 1673. In 1779, Jean Baptiste Point du Sable, <u>whose</u> origins were from Haiti, built the first permanent settlement. This was the beginning of one of our <u>principal</u> cities. In 1803, Fort Dearborn was built on the <u>site</u>. The fort was destroyed during the War of 1812 but rebuilt in 1816. Chicago officially became a city in 1837. We do not know exactly where the name "Chicago" comes from, but <u>oral</u> tradition among area Indian tribes reveals that the word was used to mean "great" in describing the Mississippi River. One hundred years ago, Chicago <u>used to</u> be a major railroad center. Today, <u>it's</u> still a great <u>capital</u> of commerce. People go <u>through</u> Chicago to get to many other destinations in the country.

Exercise E (p. 148)

Michael was more worried <u>than</u> his classmates about his grade in English. He did not want to <u>lose</u> any time, so he went to the tutoring center for help. <u>There</u> he was <u>counseled</u> by the head tutor, who encouraged him not to <u>waste</u> any time. Michael kept a weekly appointment and wrote a <u>whole</u> essay each time he met with his tutor. He found that the work he was doing in his <u>course</u> improved while he was in the tutoring center, and he was much <u>further</u> along in his writing because he never missed a session. He did very well on his final exam; all of his extra work was not in <u>vain</u>. Michael found that persistence was a big part of the <u>recipe</u> for success.

Exercise F (p. 149)

The <u>principal</u> airport in my country is located in a valley surrounded by mountains. The <u>site</u> is said to be one of the most dangerous areas for landing a <u>plane</u>. In the <u>past</u>, <u>too</u> many small aircraft <u>used to</u> take off in less <u>than</u> ideal conditions. Today, few pilots <u>choose</u> to take off in bad <u>weather</u>, and aircraft are usually <u>stationary</u> in times of severe storms.

Mastery Test (p. 150)

1.   B
2.   B
3.   B
4.   A
5.   A
6.   B
7.   A
8.   A
9.   A
10.   A